# MATH
# MENAGERIE

**Drawings by Mark A. Binn**
Illustrated with photographs

# MATH MENAGERIE

## by Robert R. Kadesch

Harper & Row, Publishers
New York, Evanston, and London

We gratefully acknowledge permission to quote from MATHEMATICAL RECREATIONS AND ESSAYS by W. W. Rouse Ball. Copyright 1942 by The Macmillan Company. Used with permission of The Macmillan Company, New York and Macmillan & Co. Ltd., London.

Jacket illustration on page 42 is from THE NEW WORLD OF MATH by George A. Boehm and FORTUNE Editors. Courtesy of Time, Inc.

# CONTENTS

# PART FIVE  Mappings and Transformations

# PART SIX  Soap-Film Mathematics

# PART SEVEN  Mathematical Machines

# MATH
# MENAGERIE

# BEFORE YOU START . . .

YOU MAY BE SURPRISED to learn that mathematics often involves experimentation. This book contains twenty-five experiments in mathematics that you can do at home. When you do them, you will literally *see* how mathematics works.

All the materials you will need are simple, inexpensive, and readily obtainable. Feel free to make substitutions for the materials listed and to make improvements in the procedures described.

The experiments are grouped in sections of three or four chapters each. It doesn't matter which section you read first, but within each section it is important to read the chapters in order. This is particularly true in the sections entitled "Probability," "Binary Numerals," and "Soap-Film Mathematics."

None of the chapters digs very far into the basic mathematics that underlies the activity. This is for you to do later. Don't be too concerned if much of the mathematics seems strange and unfamiliar to you. It's useful and exciting to explore new ideas in mathematics—you may discover that the old familiar ideas are suddenly clearer.

# PART ONE Probability

## 1 PASCAL'S PROBABILITY PINBALL

YOU'VE PROBABLY NEVER played a probability pinball machine. There are no flashing lights, no bells, no "tilt" indicator. It can be played with one ball or a thousand.

Probability pinball is a fascinating game that can teach you about the laws of probability. When a single ball travels through a probability pinball machine, the path it takes is usually different each time. But if a thousand or more balls are used, their performance *as a group* will follow a definite pattern, one that recurs time after time.

To test this, obtain several small packages of BB shot and 60 to 360 pins—depending on the complexity of the pinball board you wish to construct. Ordinary straight pins will serve admirably, but you may want to use the more elegant glass-headed pins. These are easier to press into a board and also will help confine the BB's. Map tacks will perhaps work even better, but these are more expensive.

You will need a piece of soft fiberboard, such as a single acoustical ceiling tile, or you can use map tacks on a board of soft pine.

The first job is to make an array of pins. Each row of pins should be staggered so that each pin is placed squarely in the gap formed by the two pins in the row above. Every second row is the same. In the

Figure 1.
Probability Pinball Machine

model shown in Figure 1 there is first a row of 15 pins, then a row of 16 pins, then 15, then 16, and so on for twenty-three rows.

The pins in a single row should be separated by a distance slightly less than the width of two BB's. This is important. With this placement, a ball that passes one row without hitting a pin is sure to hit a pin in the next row. Adjacent rows should be spaced so that the slant distance between the pins is approximately the same as the distance from pin to pin in a single row. It is a good idea to draw a grid on the board before you start or to paste down a sheet of graph paper to use as a guide.

Make a funnel-like opening at the top of the board to introduce the BB's into the center of the top row of pins. At the bottom of the board there should be an individual slot or bin for each space between the pins in the last row. If you plan to roll only one BB at a time, your probability pinball machine is now complete. If you plan to use a great many BB's at the same time, you will need a frame around the board and a plastic cover to keep the balls from spilling.

Place the board at a slight angle to the tabletop and run a single BB through the maze of pins. The BB will dance and jig, first one way and then the other, in a completely unpredictable way. It may end up coming out at the center of the bottom row of pins, and then again it may come out near the side. The next BB will very likely do something quite different.

Look at it this way. As a BB comes through the gap between two pins in the top row, it has equal chances to go to the right or to the left of the pin in the row below. If the BB goes to the left, for ex-

4

ample, it encounters a third-row pin in the middle of the second-row gap, and so on down the board. As the BB comes through each horizontal row of pins, it has equal chances of jumping a half space to the left or a half space to the right.

The behavior of a single BB is not predictable, but the behavior of a large number of BB's *is* fairly predictable. Each time a thousand BB's are run through the machine, the BB's in the bins form about the same pattern. The greatest number of BB's is usually found in the center bin and the least number in the last bin on either side. You will learn to recognize this pattern.

An analyis of this pattern was made by a seventeenth-century French mathematician, Blaise Pascal. The machine we have built might be called Pascal's probability pinball machine.

Pascal devised a triangle of numbers similar to the one in Figure 2. Although only seven rows of numbers are shown, the triangular array can be extended downward as far as you please.

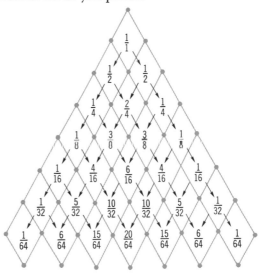

Figure 2.
Pascal's Triangle

Pascal's triangle may seem quite complicated at first, but it has such wide application that it is well worth knowing how to make it.

Starting at the top, in the space at the apex of the triangle, write the number 1 (or $\frac{1}{1}$). All the numbers below can be found, row by row, by using a definite rule. Each number appears in a diamond-shaped space, and this diamond touches either one or two other diamonds in the row above. The rule states that each number (except for the number $\frac{1}{1}$ in the first row) is half the sum of the numbers appearing in the touching diamonds in the row above. Since each second-row space touches only one space above, each second-row number is half the first-row number. Once the second-row numbers are known, the third-row numbers can be filled in, and so on down as many rows as you care to go.

Notice that the sum of the fractions in each row is 1. Notice also that the fractions are written so that the denominators in each row are the same. This makes the denominator in each row twice as large as that in the row above. Finally, the numerators in each row added together equal the denominator for that row, as they must if all the numbers in a row are to add up to 1.

The numbers appearing in Pascal's triangle are important in a wide variety of situations. One of these is our pinball machine. Perhaps you have noticed that the structure of the large triangle is the same as that of the pinball machine. Each vertex of a diamond-shaped space in the triangle could represent one of the pins in the pinball machine.

In Figure 3 we combine the two—the original pinball machine from Figure 1 and Pascal's triangle from

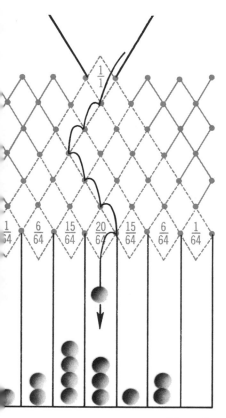

Figure 3.
Path of a Single BB Through the Machine

Figure 2. Suppose that a very large number of BB's were to start at the top and roll through the space marked $\frac{1}{1}$ in Figure 3. Each number in Pascal's triangle tells us what fraction of a very large number of BB's will roll through that particular space. If a hundred BB's are rolled through the machine, approximately $\frac{1}{2} \times 100$, or 50, will roll through the second-row space on the left, marked $\frac{1}{2}$ in Pascal's triangle. If a thousand BB's are used, approximately $\frac{1}{2} \times 1000$, or 500, will roll through this space. The word "approximately" is used because you cannot expect *exactly* half to roll through the space marked $\frac{1}{2}$. As the number of BB's used becomes larger and larger, the fraction that actually will roll through this space will come closer and closer to the value of $\frac{1}{2}$. This is why all the fractions appearing in Pascal's triangle refer to a very large number of BB's and not to any limited number that you can roll through the machine.

There is another way to look at the meaning of these fractions. Each fraction can be said to represent the probability that a *single* BB will roll through a space. Thus a single BB has a probability of $\frac{1}{2}$ to roll through the second-row space on the left, and a probability of $\frac{6}{64}$ to roll through the space second from the left in the seventh row. Whether we think of these fractions as applying to a very large number of BB's or to a single BB, the meaning is precisely the same.

The rule given earlier for filling in the numbers in Pascal's triangle makes no apparent sense, but in the case of the pinball machine it is possible to understand why each fraction represents the proper probability. Consider any given space. A ball rolling

7

through this space may have arrived there by any one of a number of possible paths. The arrows in Figure 2 suggest these paths. Each of the possible paths that start from the top and eventually lead into this space is equally likely to be taken by the ball. That is, no single route is favored over any of the others. Because of this, the probability of a ball rolling through the space will depend upon the total number of possible paths through that space. The greater the number of paths, the greater the likelihood that a ball will arrive at the space. Each numerator is simply the number of different paths leading to the space. Each denominator is the total number of paths leading to the row in which the space is located. Check both of these statements for the space marked ⅜ and then for a space in a lower row. The first number divided by the second must give the fraction of the very large number of BB's arriving at a particular row that will pass through one particular space in this row.

It is interesting to play the machine over and over to see to what extent the results for a few BB's will differ from the results expected for a very great number of BB's. Although the behavior of a single ball cannot be predicted, we can specify the probability of its passing through one space or another by the fractions that appear in Pascal's triangle. These fractions approach actualities only for an extremely large number of balls.

Pascal's probability triangle comes up again in the next three chapters.

# 2 TOSS A COIN

WHENEVER YOU FLIP a coin, it behaves differently. You cannot possibly flip a coin in exactly the same way time after time. The general motion of the hand, the upward thrust of the thumb, the point on the coin pushed by the thumb—all these factors and many others vary considerably from one toss to the next.

The fact that so many things influence the toss of a coin—none of which can be accurately controlled —makes it impossible to determine in advance whether you will get heads or tails.

The laws of probability are the same for tossing a coin as they are for the pinball machine described in the previous chapter. The equal chances for a head or a tail in a single toss correspond exactly to the even chances for a BB to bounce to the right or left as it passes through one row of pins. The probabilities for heads or tails in six tosses of a coin (or one toss of six coins) are the same as those for the passage of a single BB through six rows of pins. In the pinball machine a bounce of the BB to the left would correspond to the toss of a head, whereas a bounce to the right would correspond to the toss of a tail.

The triangle on the left in Figure 4 shows the possible results for tosses of a single coin for any number up to six tosses. The triangle on the right is the same as the Pascal triangle in the previous chapter. Pascal's triangle shows the probabilities for each combination of heads and tails found in the corresponding space in the triangle at the left. Thus we find that there is 1 chance in 64 (a probability of $\frac{1}{64}$) to get six heads in a row. There are 6 chances in 64 (a probability of $\frac{6}{64}$) to get five heads and one tail in any order in six consecutive tosses. As with the pinball machine, these probabilities can only be realized for a very large number of groups of six tosses.

Toss a coin six times. In which "bin" in Figure 4 does your result fall? Repeat the tosses in *sets of six*. See whether your results correspond to Pascal's probability triangle.

Notice that in six consecutive tosses you can expect to get three heads and three tails (in any order) only $\frac{20}{64}$, or $\frac{5}{16}$ of the time. This means that if we toss a coin six times and continue to toss it for, say, 640 sets of six tosses, in about 200 of these sets we would toss three heads and three tails.

The larger the number of tosses in any set, the less the probability for an equal number of heads and tails. This may seem strange, but it is verified by Pascal's triangle. It is true because a greater number of tosses in one set gives a greater variety of possibilities for unequal numbers of heads and tails.

Figure 4.
Possibilities and Probabilities
for Six Tosses of a Coin

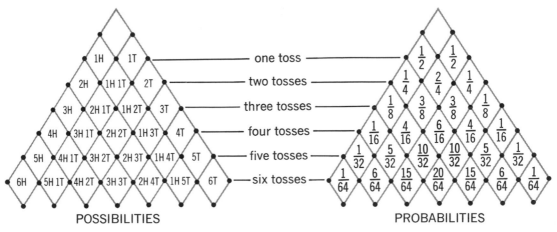

POSSIBILITIES                                     PROBABILITIES

# 3 THE BASEBALL PROBABILITY DIAMOND

Suppose the World Series is about to begin. You are wondering which team will win. You can play the Series on paper, game by game, and calculate the mathematical odds for your team to win at each step.

Let's say it's the Angels against the Mets. How each game will go, pitch by pitch, inning by inning, is extremely complicated. An enormous number of factors contribute to a team's winning or losing—from the condition of the starting pitcher's elbow to that of the infield turf. To make any headway at all in analyzing the Series, the entire situation will have to be simplified greatly. Let us assume that the skills and conditions of the two teams are an absolutely even match, that each game is a toss-up.

A hypothetical World Series played on this basis will turn out the same as it would if a toss of a coin were to determine each day's winner. Before the first game, each team's chances of winning the Series are the same. But how difficult is it to come from behind and win the Series after losing the first game? After losing the first two games? How much better is it to have dropped the first two games than to be behind three games to one?

These and all other possible situations can be analyzed by using Pascal's triangle. The outcome of the

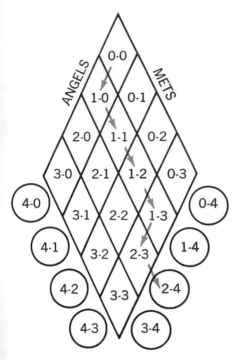

Figure 5.
Pascal's Baseball Diamond
Showing Possible Outcomes

Series will be determined on the basis of probabilities that are the same as for the toss of a coin or the bounce of a BB in the probability pinball machine. There is one important difference, however. The Series ends when one team has won four games. The total number of games played might be four, five, six, or seven.

With this best-of-seven system, the lower-left- and lower-right-hand corners of the probability triangle do not apply because these spaces represent games that would not be played. One of the two teams would already have won four games. So Pascal's triangle becomes instead Pascal's diamond, a baseball probability diamond.

Figure 5 shows each of the possible outcomes after every day's play. The won-lost situations shown inside the circles represent possible final outcomes. There are seventy possible routes through the diamond, representing the seventy possible ways to play the Series. (Can you convince yourself that there are only seventy different ways to play the Series?) One such route is indicated by the arrows. In this case the Mets won the Series four games to two.

The Pascal's diamond at the left in Figure 6 shows probabilities that correspond to the won-lost spaces in the diamond shown above. These probabilities apply only before the first game is played. The rule for obtaining the probabilities shown inside the circles is changed because the Series terminates when one team has won four games. That is, a probability written in a circle does not contribute to the probability shown in another circle below it. For this reason, most of the circled probabilities are not the same as those shown in the corresponding diamond-shaped spaces of a full Pascal's triangle.

Now suppose that the Mets have won the first game. The probability that they can go on and win the Series must now be greater than ½. The probabilities for each of the remaining possibilities must now be recalculated starting with a 1 in the Angels-0–Mets-1 space. Similarly, if the Mets win the first two games, a 1 placed in the 0-2 space starts the chain of probabilities for this situation. Both of these situations are illustrated in Figure 6. The calculations for other possibilities would be handled in a similar way.

In each of the three situations, notice that the sum of all the probabilities shown in the circles is equal to 1. This indicates that the Series is certain to be completed in one way or another. The sum of all the circled probabilities on each team's side of the diamond is that team's probability for winning.

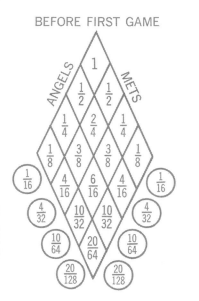

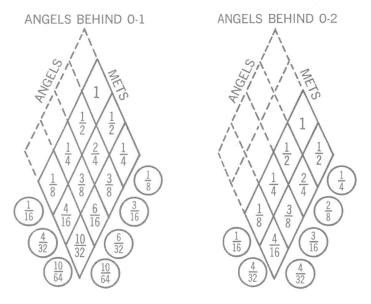

Figure 6. Probability Diamonds for Three Situations

The number of different ways the remaining games can be won and lost can be counted just as we counted the different paths for a BB through the pinball machine. These are indicated by the sum of the numerators of the circled fractions. The denominators remain the same—they double row by row. Thus we can determine that there are 70 ways to play the Series, starting before the first game, 35 ways to complete the Series after one game has been played, and 15 ways to finish the Series if one team has won the first two games. Each of these ways is equally probable. The team with the greater chance of winning is the team that has a greater number of ways to win.

A World Series between evenly matched teams could be played on a pinball machine in which the bins were moved up to conform to Pascal's diamond. Or the toss of a coin could be used to represent the game, each head being an Angels' win and each tail a victory for the Mets.

But suppose the Angels and Mets are not evenly matched. Suppose everyone agrees that the Angels have the edge and further that their probability for winning each game is $\frac{3}{5}$. The probability for the Mets to win in each game would then be $\frac{2}{5}$.

The Pascal's diamond of probabilities would have to be revised. Instead of taking $\frac{1}{2}$ of each of the probabilities in the two spaces above, you would take $\frac{3}{5}$ of the number above and to the right of the space and $\frac{2}{5}$ of the number above and to the left, then add the results to get the fraction that goes in the space.

In such a diamond the figure on the right in the third row would be $\frac{4}{25}$, and on the left $\frac{9}{25}$. In the center is $\frac{12}{25}$, which is the sum of $\frac{3}{5}$ of the $\frac{2}{5}$ above and to the right and $\frac{2}{5}$ of the $\frac{3}{5}$ above and to the left.

The second figure from the left in the fourth row of the diamond will be $^{54}/_{125}$. Now complete the diamond and find the probabilities for the Mets or the Angels to win the Series by the various combinations of wins and losses.

# 4 ROLL A PROBABILITY CURVE

PROBABILITIES PLAY a part in our lives every day. The weatherman says, for example, that there will be a 10 percent chance of rain tomorrow. There is also the probability that your English teacher will give you a surprise quiz. Men are drafted into the armed forces by a lottery system that involves the element of chance. Tossing coins, playing cards, landing on Park Place in a game of Monopoly—all these depend on the laws of probability.

In many situations the role of chance is less clear. Take for instance an experiment in which a marble is rolled on a carpet to determine how far it will go on successive rolls. Although the experiment is far from dramatic, the data when plotted on a graph will exhibit a bell-shaped form that may surprise you. This fairly smooth bell-shape is the famous probability curve. Once this curve has been obtained, the probable distance of the next roll of the marble can be determined.

To perform the experiment, first build a simple ramp like the one in Figure 7. The ramp should have a horizontal platform at the top so that a marble can be started from the same height each time. Two boards with an identical slope, nailed less than the width of a marble apart, will give the ramp a groove to control the direction of roll.

In spite of nearly identical starting conditions, the rolling marble does not go the same distance on the carpet each time. The tufts in the carpet present varying resistance to the marble with each roll. Sometimes these irregularities slow the marble quickly, sometimes not so quickly. The distances will, however, tend to group around some average length.

Measure the distance rolled by the marble on 50, 100, or an even greater number of rolls. Record only the nearest inch mark for the length of each roll. Now list the number of times the marble stopped closest to each inch. (If most of the distances vary by only 4" to 6", record to the closest half-inch mark.)

The bar graph in Figure 8 shows the results of 228 rolls of the marble on the surface shown in Figure 7. The ball rolled closest to the 25" mark only two times. Six times the ball stopped nearest the 26" line, and so on. The height of each bar represents the total number of rolls for each inch mark. A line connecting the tops of the bars would form a rather smooth

Figure 7.
Experimental Setup

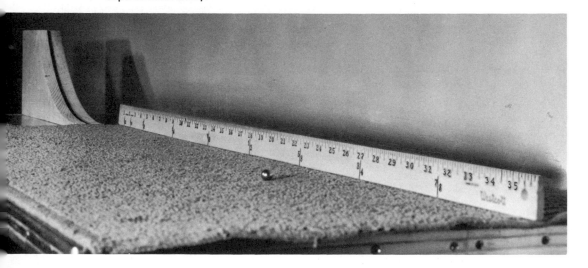

bell-shaped curve. The curve in Figure 8 represents the theoretical probability curve, a curve that the bars would fit more closely for an extremely large number of trials.

To calculate the average distance the marble rolled, multiply each distance, in whole numbers of inches, by the number of times the marble stopped closest to that distance. Add all the numbers obtained and divide the sum by the total number of rolls. In our experiment the average distance is very close to 30.5″, the peak of the curve.

The width of the bell-shaped curve is as important as the average distance. If this width is small, the chances are excellent that any single measurement will lie close to the average. If this width is large, more of the measurements will lie some distance from the average.

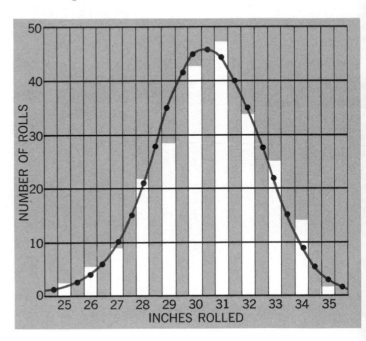

Figure 8.
Results of Experiment

18

Now use the bell-shaped curve to predict the behavior of the next marble to be rolled down the incline. What is the probability, for example, that it will roll 28″? In Figure 8 we see that the marble traveled this distance in 22 of the 228 previous rolls. The probability for the marble to repeat this distance on the next roll is therefore $\frac{22}{228}$ or 0.096.

The bell-shaped curve should look familiar to you. Doesn't it remind you of the distribution of BB's in the bins of the probability pinball machine? A bar graph representing the values of the numbers in one of the lower rows in Pascal's triangle would have a similar curve. The lower the row used, the closer the curve comes to the theoretical bell.

All these experiments are related—the pinball, coin tossing, World Series, and now the roll of a marble across a carpet.

# PART TWO Binary Numerals

## 5 BINARY ARITHMETIC

DID YOU KNOW THAT $1 + 1 = 10$? The addition has been performed perfectly—not in the familiar numeration system but in the simpler system of binary numerals.

In the binary system there are only two digits, 0 and 1. This makes it easy to add and to multiply. The symbols 0 and 1 represent zero and one, just as you might think they would. By using binary arithmetic, humans can instruct machines to add and subtract, multiply and divide. Although computing machines must be taught just as you or I, the machines can perform such operations with lightning speed, having once learned the system. This is their major advantage.

Once you learn a little binary arithmetic—which is interesting in itself—you will have a better idea of how giant electronic computers function. The following two chapters utilize binary numerals to develop a punched-card system and to help solve a mystifying mathematical puzzle.

To understand the binary numeration system, it is helpful to review some important features of the numeration system we all use every day. This is called a base-ten numeration system. In it, there are ten digits, written 0, 1, 2, 3, 4, 5, 6, 7, 8, and 9. We group numbers by tens. For example, the symbol 10 represents a single group of ten objects. The position of the digit 1 tells us this. Ten groups of ten objects each is represented by the symbol 100. Ten groups of a hundred objects each is written 1000. The digit 1 represents one, ten, a hundred, a thousand, ten thousand, a hundred thousand, or a million, depending upon its position. It may be in the units place, the tens place, the hundreds place, and so on.

We can easily develop an entirely different numeration system simply by changing the number of objects that form a group. Suppose we change this grouping number to two. Then the symbol 1 represents one object just as before, but the symbol 10 represents two objects, not ten, and 11 represents 10 plus 1, or three. If we have two groups of two objects each (rather than ten groups of ten objects each), we write this number as 100 (four). Two groups of objects, each group consisting of two groups of two objects each, is represented by 1000 (eight), and so on. This is the binary numeration system. Only two digits are needed, 0 and 1, because there are just two objects in each group, rather than ten. The binary grouping scheme is illustrated in Figure 9. A group

Figure 9.
Binary Grouping
10 Groups of 10 Groups of 10

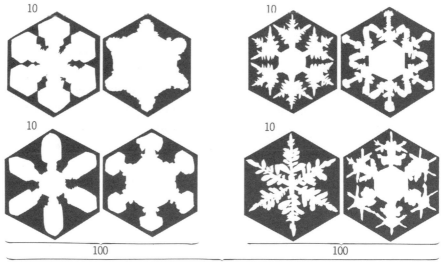

10          10

10          10

100          100

1000

of two snowflakes is written as 10, two groups of 10 each is 100, and two groups of 100 flakes is 1000.

To continue, two groups of eight is sixteen, or 10000; two groups of sixteen is thirty-two, written as 100000; and two of these groups is sixty-four, and so on.

We now have the following binary representations:

| | | |
|---:|---:|:---|
| 1 = | 1 | one |
| 10 = | 2 | two |
| 100 = | 4 | four |
| 1000 = | 8 | eight |
| 10000 = | 16 | sixteen |
| 100000 = | 32 | thirty-two |
| 1000000 = | 64 | sixty-four |

Notice that each of these numbers is just twice the preceding number.

Now consider the numeral 101010. The first place on the right in a binary numeral is the units place. Going left from the units place, the next is the twos place, the next the fours place, then the eights place, the sixteens place, and the thirty-twos place. Just as the numeral 306 in the familiar decimal system represents $300 + 6$, the binary numeral 101010 represents the binary addition of $100000 + 1000 + 10$. This turns out to be thirty-two plus eight plus two, or forty-two in all.

Practice reading the following binary numerals: 1100, 10011, 101101. Then try constructing the binary numerals in order, from zero to sixty-three, to gain a better appreciation of the pattern that develops as you proceed. Check your results with the numbers shown in the table that follows:

| Base-Ten | Binary | Base-Ten | Binary | Base-Ten | Binary | Base-Ten | Binary |
|---|---|---|---|---|---|---|---|
| 0 | 000000 | 16 | 010000 | 32 | 100000 | 48 | 110000 |
| 1 | 000001 | 17 | 010001 | 33 | 100001 | 49 | 110001 |
| 2 | 000010 | 18 | 010010 | 34 | 100010 | 50 | 110010 |
| 3 | 000011 | 19 | 010011 | 35 | 100011 | 51 | 110011 |
| 4 | 000100 | 20 | 010100 | 36 | 100100 | 52 | 110100 |
| 5 | 000101 | 21 | 010101 | 37 | 100101 | 53 | 110101 |
| 6 | 000110 | 22 | 010110 | 38 | 100110 | 54 | 110110 |
| 7 | 000111 | 23 | 010111 | 39 | 100111 | 55 | 110111 |
| 8 | 001000 | 24 | 011000 | 40 | 101000 | 56 | 111000 |
| 9 | 001001 | 25 | 011001 | 41 | 101001 | 57 | 111001 |
| 10 | 001010 | 26 | 011010 | 42 | 101010 | 58 | 111010 |
| 11 | 001011 | 27 | 011011 | 43 | 101011 | 59 | 111011 |
| 12 | 001100 | 28 | 011100 | 44 | 101100 | 60 | 111100 |
| 13 | 001101 | 29 | 011101 | 45 | 101101 | 61 | 111101 |
| 14 | 001110 | 30 | 011110 | 46 | 101110 | 62 | 111110 |
| 15 | 001111 | 31 | 011111 | 47 | 101111 | 63 | 111111 |

Once you are familiar with the reading and writing of binary numerals, it is simple to learn to add and to multiply them. Addition and multiplication can each be described by just four equations:

$$0 + 0 = 0 \qquad 0 \times 0 = 0$$
$$0 + 1 = 1 \qquad 0 \times 1 = 0$$
$$1 + 0 = 1 \qquad 1 \times 0 = 0$$
$$1 + 1 = 10 \qquad 1 \times 1 = 1$$

The only strange-looking relationship is the one at the lower left, which tells us in binary figures that one plus one equals two. With these results in mind, and with your knowledge of "carrying over" into the next place, you should be able to check the following:

```
   10          11          101
  +10         +11          +10
  ───         ───          ───
  100         110          111
```

```
       101              110
      ×101             ×111
      ───              ───
       101              110
       000              110
       101              110
      ─────            ──────
      11001            101010
```

Expressed in base-ten numerals, these problems are written:

```
    2           3           5
   +2          +3          +2
   ──          ──          ──
    4           6           7
```

```
       5            6
      ×5           ×7
      ──           ──
      25           42
```

In the two chapters that follow it is assumed that you are now an expert with binary numerals!

# 6  A CODED CARD DECK

ELECTRONIC COMPUTING machines serve many valuable purposes in today's world of science and business. Many of these machines use the binary numeration system. There are good reasons automatic computers operate so easily with a system using the two digits 0 and 1. In some machines, mathematical calculations can be performed using switches that are either *on* or *off*. *ON* can represent the digit 1; *OFF* can represent 0. Other machines contain magnets which, like compass needles, have north-seeking and south-seeking ends. When the magnetization is made to point in one direction, it represents a stored 0; when reversed it represents a stored 1. Still other computers have components which can either be electrically conducting or nonconducting. Anything which can exist in two basic states or conditions is a natural for use with the binary numeration system.

A pack of punched cards is not a true computer, but such cards can show the principle on which a computer operates. Cards can be coded with many kinds of information. When information is placed on cards in this way, it is said to be stored there. Data can then be retrieved in a variety of ways. For example, a single punch in a card may be either a hole or a slot. A hole can represent the digit 0, a slot the digit 1. Since a card can be punched with either of two basic shapes, a hole or a slot, each such punch performs the same function as a computer switch or magnet.

By making your own set of punched cards, you will learn a few of the many uses to which these cards may be put. Obtain at least sixty-four 3″ by 5″ file cards. You also need a hole-puncher, scissors, and a knitting needle.

The code you will punch and cut into the cards will represent the binary numeration system. A hole will represent the digit 0 and a slot will represent the digit 1. Make a slot by first punching a hole, then cutting the card away above the hole.

First, however, punch a row of six holes along the top of each of the sixty-four cards. Space these holes approximately ½″ apart and about a ½″ from the top edge of the card. To make the cards uniform, make a master card and then punch all the other cards through the holes in the master.

When the cards are punched, cut slots in the proper positions to represent the binary numerals from zero through sixty-three. The number forty-six, or 101110, is shown punched and cut appropriately in Figure 10. It will also be helpful to cut off the upper-right-hand corners of each of the cards. This way no card can be turned over or turned upside down without your noticing it immediately.

Until you become more familiar with the binary numeration system, it might be wise to print on each card the equivalent number according to the base-ten system.

Now let's see what can be done with the cards. First, shuffle them as you would a deck of playing cards. You can place them in numerical order by

Figure 10.
Card Number Forty-six or 101110

using only six simple operations. Spear a knitting needle through the deck of cards, in the hole farthest to the right—the units place. Lift all the cards that are on the needle out of the pack. These will be the cards that contain holes in this place rather than slots. In performing this operation, hold the pack very loosely in your left hand while shaking the needle rapidly with your right hand. All the cards with slots will fall back into your hand. Place the cards lifted by the needle in front of the others. Now repeat this procedure five times with the entire

Figure 11.
Arranging the Cards in Order

deck, working to the left in the row of holes and slots. Lo and behold! The cards are now in proper order, zero through sixty-three, starting at the front.

You can also select any one of the cards you desire from a jumbled deck. Suppose you want Card Number Forty-six. Forty-six in binary notation is written 101110. First spear the units place. The desired card is among those that remain on the needle, since Number Forty-six has a hole in the units place rather than a slot. Set the other cards aside and spear the sixteens place in the cards that remain. Again the desired card is among those that remain on the needle. In succession, spear the twos place, or second slot to the left, the third slot, the fourth, and the sixth. In each of these instances the desired card is among those that fall. As you spear the sixth slot, only Card Number Forty-six will fall.

These features of the card pack are useful in making an information-retrieval system, better known as an index file. Let 000000 stand for the letter *A*, 000001 for *B*, and so on. Any number of cards representing a particular letter can be used, of course. Since there are only twenty-six letters in the alphabet, Card Number 011010 can be used to begin a second alphabetical listing.

To put your binary-index file to actual use, all desired information must be placed on the cards and coded alphabetically. A card labeled *Binary Numeral System* can be readily found, together with all the other cards beginning with the letter *B*, simply by separating the 000001 cards from the rest. However, in the system the letter *B* cards would not themselves be in alphabetical order, nor would those that begin with any other letter of the alphabet. These cards can only classify information by the first letter. If you were to alphabetize according to the first two letters, a ten-digit system would be required. That is, *Aa* would be represented by the 0000000000 card, *Ab* by the 0000000001 card, and so on. Six hundred and seventy-six cards would be required to represent all possible two-letter combinations.

Another use can be made of the card deck. Each of the hole and slot positions can represent one in a set of six characteristics of some kind. For example, suppose you classify your classmates according to six characteristics. Let these be male, female; brown-eyed, blue-eyed; tall, short; blond, brunette; freckled, not freckled; and curly-haired, straight-haired. For each characteristic there must be two and only two possibilities. In each instance let 0 represent the first-named characteristic and 1 the second-named. Prepare a card for each member of the class, using each of the six holes or slots to represent one of the characteristics. Now it will be an easy task to find the number of straight-haired, freckled, blond, short, blue-eyed boys in your class or, for that matter, the number who have any other combination of characteristics.

Perhaps you will find still other uses for your binary-coded card deck. See what you can do.

# 7 THE TOWER OF HANOI

GAMES AND PUZZLES can provide hours of entertainment. When one of them can be analyzed mathematically, it becomes even more interesting. Although the famous puzzle of the Tower of Hanoi can be solved without mathematical analysis, it is much simpler with the help of the binary numeration system.

The puzzle consists of a base with three pegs. On one of the pegs there is a tower of eight disks. Each disk is a different size; the largest is at the bottom, the next largest directly above, and so on, with the eighth and smallest disk at the top.

Figure 12.
Tower of Hanoi Puzzle

The problem is to move the entire tower one disk at a time to either one of the other two pegs. No disk must ever be allowed to rest on a disk smaller than itself.

Construct the disks needed for this puzzle from

heavy cardboard or other suitable material. Pound three nails through the bottom of a wooden base, to act as pegs, making sure they are separated by a distance greater than the diameter of the largest disk. The pegs aren't absolutely necessary; any eight objects of graded size can simply be stacked one on top of the other. If you prefer, you may purchase the puzzle at a toy counter or novelty shop.

An interesting story about the Tower is related by W. W. Rouse Ball in his book *Mathematical Recreations and Essays* (The Macmillan Company, New York, 1956) :

> In the great temple at Benares . . . beneath the dome which marks the center of the world, rests a brass plate in which are fixed three diamond needles, each a cubit high and as thick as the body of a bee. On one of these needles, at the Creation, God placed sixty-four disks of pure gold, the largest disk resting on the brass plate, and the others getting smaller and smaller up to the top one. This is the Tower of Bramah. Day and night unceasingly the priests transfer the disks from one diamond needle to another according to the fixed immutable laws of Bramah, which require that the priest on duty must not move more than one disk at a time and that he must place this disk on a needle so that there is no smaller disk below it. When the sixty-four disks shall have been thus transferred from the needle on which at the Creation God placed them to one of the other needles, tower, temple and Brahmins alike will crumble into dust, and with a thunderclap the world will vanish.

Your task will be much easier than the priests', since you will have only eight disks in your tower.

As soon as you complete construction of the puzzle,

try transferring just three of the disks onto one peg to get an idea how the game works. Once you've accomplished this, the fourth disk can be moved to the empty peg. Now you have the problem of moving the first three disks all over again, this time to the top of the fourth disk. And now the fifth disk can be moved to an empty peg, and the first four disks must be moved over to the top of the fifth disk.

It isn't easy to keep the necessary moves straight in your mind. You'll find that moving the first two disks requires three moves. To move three disks requires a total of seven moves, and four disks require fifteen moves. Each additional disk to be moved necessitates as many more moves as you have already made plus one.

A tower of eight disks can be transferred in no less than two hundred and fifty-five moves. The number of transfers required of the Brahmin priests in moving the sixty-four golden disks is 18,446,744,073,-709,551,615.

Try the puzzle before reading further. The description that follows provides a foolproof scheme for finding each move. The key is provided by the binary numeration system.

Number the eight disks one through eight, starting with the smallest and ending with the largest disk. Now write in a column on a sheet of paper the binary numerals from one through two hundred and fifty-five (1–11111111).

These binary numerals tell you which disk to move and where to move it for each of the two hundred fifty-five moves. You are only concerned with the first two 1's in each binary number. Their positions show what move to make.

As you read the binary numerals from right to left, the position of the first 1 tells you which disk to move. If it is in the first place on the right, move disk one, the smallest. If it is in the second place, move disk two; third place, disk three, and so on.

The position of the second 1 identifies a disk on top of one of the two **pegs** that were originally empty. If this second 1 is in the second position, it indicates disk two. If it is in third position, it indicates disk three.

The number of 0's between the two 1's shows where the moving disk is to go. If there is an even number of 0's or none (zero, two, four, or six), the disk moves to the position indicated by the second 1. Thus 1001 means move disk one to the top of disk four. If there are an odd number of 0's (one, three, or five), the disk moves to the position *not* indicated by the second 1. Thus 1010 means move disk two to the remaining peg, *not* to disk four. If there is just a single 1 in the binary numeral, move the indicated disk to an empty peg.

The first fifteen moves are:

| | |
|---|---|
| 1 | move disk one to an empty peg |
| 10 | move disk two to an empty peg |
| 11 | place disk one on disk two |
| 100 | move disk three to an empty peg |
| 101 | place disk one **not** on disk three |
| 110 | place disk two on disk three |
| 111 | place disk one on disk two |
| 1000 | move disk four to an empty peg |
| 1001 | place disk one on disk four |
| 1010 | place disk two **not** on disk four |
| 1011 | place disk one on disk two |
| 1100 | place disk three on disk four |
| 1101 | place disk one **not** on disk three |
| 1110 | place disk two on disk three |
| 1111 | place disk one on disk two |

Now follow the instructions of the binary numerals through the rest of the two hundred and fifty-five moves for the complete transfer of the Tower.

# PART THREE Unusual Numbers

## 8 HOW BIG IS A GOOGOL?

WHAT IS THE LARGEST number you can think of? Is it the national debt, the number of grains of sand on all the beaches of the world, the number of raindrops that fall in a year, or the number of stars in the sky? How could you write a very, very large number without spending the rest of your life doing it? This is a mathematical "thought" experiment, to be performed in your own mind.

A schoolboy named Pasha, so the mythical story goes, was once asked to write the largest number he could. He first wrote a 1 with a hundred 0's behind it and called this number a googol. A googol is certainly an extremely large number. In fact, it is larger by far than the number of sand grains on all the beaches or the number of stars in the sky.

A mathematician would write the googol as $10^{100}$. This is merely a symbol. The 100 at the upper-right-hand corner of the number 10 indicates that a googol is the same as a hundred 10's multiplied by each other. One googol $= 10^{100} = 10 \times 10 \times 10 \times 10 \times 10 \times \cdots$ (with a hundred of these 10's appearing before you stop). In the same way, $2^3$ means $2 \times 2 \times 2$, and $10^4$ means $10 \times 10 \times 10 \times 10$.

All the words that have ever been printed number about $10^{16}$. The number of stars in the sky is at least as great as $10^{20}$. The number of oxygen atoms in a thimbleful of air is about $10^{27}$.

Obviously you can write a number larger than the googol merely by writing a 1 with more than a hundred 0's behind it. A good mathematician, however, looks for an easier way to write large numbers.

Pasha also invented the googolplex. He said it was a 1 with a googol of 0's behind it. Thus it is very much larger than the googol. In fact, the googolplex has so many 0's behind the 1 that Pasha doubted if anyone could ever write them all down or find the space to do it.

Mathematical shorthand can also be used to represent the googolplex. Since 1 googol $= 10^{100}$ and is the number 1 with a hundred 0's behind it, a 1 with a googol of 0's behind it is $10^{googol}$. Therefore:

$$1 \text{ googolplex} = 10^{googol} = (10^{10})^{100}$$

You can think of a googolplex as a googol of 10's multiplied together.

Sir Arthur Eddington once proposed a theory that required that the total number of hydrogen nuclei in the entire universe be $10^{79}$ and that there also be the same number of electrons. This number is somewhat less than a googol and a very small fraction of a googolplex.

The googolplex is dwarfed by the Mega and the Megiston, two more numbers invented by Pasha. If we write a number such as 2 inside a triangle, he said, let it be agreed that this means 2 multiplied by itself two times. That is:

$$\triangle{2} = 2^2$$

In like manner:

$$\triangle{10} = 10^{10} = 10 \times 10 \times 10 \times 10 \times 10 \times 10 \times 10 \times 10 \times 10 \times 10$$

Any number inside a square would mean that number in that many triangles, each triangle written inside the other. For example:

$\boxed{2}$ means 2 in two triangles

or

 $= 4^4 = 256$

$\boxed{3}$ means 3 in three triangles

or

, and so on.

Finally, $\textcircled{2}$ signifies 2 in two squares, $\textcircled{3}$ signifies 3 in three squares, and similarly for any other number in a circle. Refer to Figure 13 to keep these definitions straight in your mind.

One Mega is the number $\textcircled{2}$. This is a number so large that it is beyond comprehension. An even larger number is $\textcircled{10}$, called a Megiston. This gi-

**Figure 13.**
**Very Large Numbers**

37

ant is staggering. Yet it is so innocent looking, so easy to write.

By now you may be able to find ways of your own to write numbers even larger than those invented by Pasha. These numbers may not be useful in the real world about us, but they may serve to measure your own imagination.

# 9 TAKE A NUMBER

TAKE A NUMBER, any number. Now square each digit and add the numbers obtained. This gives you a new number. Square each digit of this new number and add the results to obtain yet another number. Proceeding in this way, sooner or later you *always* obtain either the number 1 or the number 58.

This is a little known oddity of our number system that is intriguing to say the least. Why should you *always* arrive either at the number 1 or the number 58? Try it out for yourself to see that it is so.

These trials constitute a mathematical experiment of a sort. Let's follow through one example to see how it goes. Start with the number 264. Remember that any other number would do as well. The squares of the digits are 4, 36, and 16, and the sum of these squares is 56. The squares of these two digits are 25 and 36, and their sum is 61. The squares of these two digits are 36 and 1 with a sum of 37. Squaring again gives 9 and 49, with a sum of 58!

It is interesting to note that if the same procedure is continued with the number 58, eight more steps of squaring and adding will produce a 58 once again. When the number 1 is obtained, the same procedure gives nothing but more 1's.

Select a number of your own. It may contain as

many digits as you wish. See if you don't eventually arrive either at the number 1 or the number 58. Continue the experiment with as many other numbers as your stamina will allow.

If you always obtain either a 1 or a 58 after having tried ten different beginning numbers—after a hundred, a thousand, or more—what does it prove? Does it *prove* that you will get either a 1 or a 58 with *any* number you might select? No, it proves nothing of the sort. Such results would certainly make the idea seem believable, and maybe it really is true. But this in itself does not prove that one of these two numbers will always appear. Perhaps it wouldn't work for some number you did not select.

When you draw the conclusion that a 1 or a 58 will always appear no matter what number you select in the beginning, the kind of logic you use is called inductive reasoning. You are attempting to draw a broad conclusion from an examination of a number of particular circumstances. But the conclusions you arrive at by inductive reasoning may or may not be correct.

For example, simply because the sun has risen each day for a long, long time does not necessarily mean that it will rise tomorrow. Chances are that it will, but the sun does not have to rise simply because it has done so in all recorded history. Similarly, if you were to toss a coin and obtain fifty heads in a row, inductive reasoning might tell you that the next toss would also give you a head. Do you think this prediction would be likely to come true?

It is possible—though somewhat difficult—to prove mathematically that either the number 1 or the number 58 will always appear by following the procedure described. This proof is far more convincing than the evidence that can be obtained by experiment, no matter how many trials are made.

# 10 FLIPS AND SPINS

ALMOST EVERYONE IS familiar with the properties of ordinary numbers. The sum of $3 + 5$ is the same as that of $5 + 3$. Likewise, $4 \times 7$ gives the same result as $7 \times 4$. This seems the most natural thing in the world. We have learned that it is so. We accept it. In short, we can add or multiply in any order; the result is the same either way.

In the mathematics of spins and flips there is also more than one order for doing things. The rotation of an object is an operation which is the counterpart of adding 3 or multiplying by 4. Unlike the operations of addition and multiplication, however, two different rotations may not give the same result if performed in reverse order.

Take a book. Any book will do. Place it in front of you, front side up and bound edge to the left as if you were about to open it and read. Now flip it over, bottom edge away from you and top edge toward you, rotating on an axis which extends across the middle of the book from left to right. This rotation leaves the back side of the book showing with its bound edge still at your left. Now rotate the book 90°, a quarter turn counterclockwise. This operation leaves the back of the book still showing but the bound edge nearest you. Make a mental note of this position of the book—back side up and bound edge toward you.

**Figure 14.**
**Flip and Spin of a Book**

These two maneuvers, the flip and the 90° spin, have, in a sense, been added together. They are two operations which have been successively applied to the book.

But now let us "add" the two operations in reverse order. Starting with the book in its original position again, first rotate it 90° counterclockwise. This leaves the book right side up with the bound edge toward you. Now perform the second operation. Flip the book over using a left-to-right axis as before so that the side nearest you becomes the far side. The book is now back side up, the bound edge away from you.

This is not the same position the book was in previously, in spite of the fact that the same two operations were performed. Before, the bound edge of the book was on the near side; this time it is located on the far side. What accounts for the difference? The two operations were performed in reverse order, and two different results were obtained.

In the case of spinning and flipping an object, we see that the order in which the operations are applied may make a difference in the outcome. In the situation illustrated, flip followed by spin does not equal spin followed by flip.

Introducing a technical word, we say that the *commutative* law (the law whereby $3 + 5 = 5 + 3$ and $4 \times 7 = 7 \times 4$) does not apply to spins and flips.

Spinning and flipping operations can be described in a systematic way. Eight basic operations can be performed: three different counterclockwise rotations, four different flips, and an eighth "operation" which consists of doing nothing to the object. We

## TABLE OF OPERATIONS

| 0 | do nothing |
|---|---|
| A | rotate 90° counterclockwise |
| B | rotate 180° counterclockwise |
| C | rotate 270° counterclockwise |
| D | flip over around D-D axis |
| E | flip over around E-E axis |
| F | flip over around F-F axis |
| G | flip over around G-G axis |

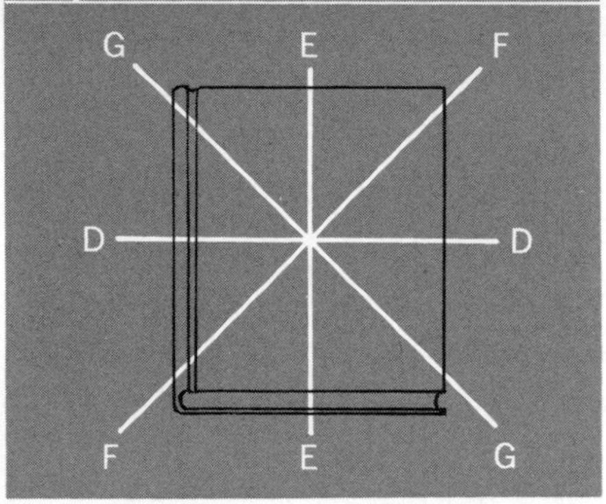

Figure 15.
Flip and Spin Operations
and Their Results

**SECOND OPERATION**

| FIRST OPERATION | 0 | A | B | C | D | E | F | G |
|---|---|---|---|---|---|---|---|---|
| **0** | 0 | A | B | C | D | E | F | G |
| **A** | A | B | C | 0 | G | F | D | E |
| **B** | B | C | 0 | A | E | D | G | F |
| **C** | C | 0 | A | B | F | G | E | D |
| **D** | D | F | E | G | 0 | B | A | C |
| **E** | E | G | D | F | B | 0 | C | A |
| **F** | F | E | G | D | C | A | 0 | B |
| **G** | G | D | F | E | A | C | B | 0 |

shall label these operations as indicated in Figure 15, in the Table of Operations. Clockwise rotations are not included because each of these produces the same result as one of the counterclockwise rotations already listed.

The square array of letters in Figure 15 shows the result of the successive application of any two of the eight operations. The first operation is given in the vertical column at the left. The second operation is given in the horizontal row across the top. The result of any two operations appears in the small square which aligns with both the first and the second operation.

The flip and rotation of the book that we performed earlier are operations D and A. The table tells us that operation D followed by operation A is equivalent to the single operation F, a flip about a diagonal axis extending from the lower left to the upper right. A reverse of the order, operation A followed by D, is equivalent to G, a flip about the other diagonal axis. Check the table by performing these operations.

Inspection of the chart shows that twenty-four of the sixty-four pairs of operations give a different result when the order of the operations is reversed.

Spin and flip operations can be used to describe the symmetry of an object such as a snowflake, flower, starfish, statue, or oil painting. Look for an operation that will leave an object in a position that is indistinguishable from the original position. The greater the number of such operations, the greater the symmetry of the object. Operation O, the do-nothing operation, would be the only such operation for an object without symmetry. For a sphere, on the other hand, each of the eight operations would leave the object looking the same as it did before the operation was performed. Thus a sphere has the maximum symmetry possible.

To investigate symmetries further, make cardboard cutouts of the letters *J*, *M*, *N*, and *I* in block-letter form. Perform each of the eight operations given in the table and determine for each letter the number of operations that leave it unchanged. Do you find one, two, two, and four such operations respectively? Although both the *M* and *N* are left unchanged by two of the eight operations, they have different kinds of symmetry. One letter is left the same for operation B, whereas the other is unchanged when operation E is performed. Furthermore, some pairs of operations performed upon the letter *M* do not obey the commutative law. Any two operations performed on the letter *N*, however, give the same result when applied in reverse order.

Each of the four letters *J*, *M*, *N*, and *I* has its own special kind of symmetry. Can you determine the kinds of symmetry shown by the remaining letters of the alphabet? Using other designs, can you identify any other types of symmetry?

# PART FOUR Menagerie of Shapes

## 11 THE BEAUTY OF MATHEMATICS

A<small>RT</small>, <small>MUSIC</small>, <small>MATHEMATICS</small>—these apparently divergent disciplines are in many ways closely related. The mathematician creates new mathematics with the same spirit as a painter expressing his ideas on canvas or a composer writing a symphony. A mathematical formula represents a relationship much like that represented by musical notes written on a sheet of paper. The striking geometrical constructions shown in Figures 16 and 17 are also representations of mathematical relationships.

The first model (Figure 16) represents a one-sheeted hyperboloid, the second (Figure 17) a hyperbolic paraboloid. These are the technical names for a surface that looks something like an hourglass and a surface that is saddle-shaped. You can visualize the surfaces involved by mentally filling in between the lengths of nylon line used in the models.

You can easily construct these models. Make the one-sheeted hyperboloid first. The model in Figure 16 can be constructed from wooden embroidery hoops 6″ in diameter. The axis of the figure is a 12″ length of dowel $\frac{7}{16}$″ in diameter. The crosspieces supporting the hoops are two dowels, 6″ long and $\frac{3}{16}$″ in diameter. Drill thirty-eight small holes in each hoop, spaced slightly more than $\frac{1}{2}$″ apart.

Choose colored fishlines to thread through the

Figure 16.
One-Sheeted Hyperboloid

47

holes of this model and that of the hyperbolic paraboloid. Select the heavier type of line in a bright, attractive color.

As you can see from Figure 16, each length of line from the upper hoop extends downward on a slant to a hole in the lower hoop. The lower hole lies about one-third of a full circle away from the position of the upper hole. If nylon lines were threaded to the lower hoop at a point more nearly halfway around the hoop, the figure would narrow at the middle more than it does in the figure shown.

Embroidery hoops of two different sizes can be used at bottom and top to make a more varied figure. Oval-shaped (elliptical) frames can also be used in place of the circular hoops. Of course any hooplike objects can be used to support the nylon line, but they must be held apart in some way or the model will collapse.

Tie a knot in the line on the inner side of one of the holes in the upper hoop. Run the line to the selected hole in the lower hoop and thread it through from the outside to the inside of the hoop. Now run the line out again through the adjacent hole and up to the first hoop. Repeat this process until the line runs through every hole in both hoops. When you have finished, you will have a striking geometric form.

We will discuss the geometry of the one-sheeted hyperboloid after we make the model of the saddle-shaped hyperbolic paraboloid. For this figure, you will need four lengths of $\frac{1}{4}''$ dowel, each about 12'' long.

The framework can be thought of as a square that has been skewed, or twisted, to form the shape in

**Figure 17.
Hyperbolic Paraboloid**

Figure 17. In this model the angles between adjacent edges of the frame are each 60°. You can skew the square as little or as much as you wish by changing these angles, but the surface in the illustration shows up particularly well.

It is simplest first to cement the dowels together to form two separate V's. Glue them so that the inside angle is 60°. After the cement has set, complete the frame by cementing the two V's together. Epoxy resin is recommended for this purpose.

Drill $\frac{1}{16}''$ holes in two opposite sides of the frame and space the holes approximately $\frac{1}{2}''$ apart. Now connect the opposite holes of the figure with fishline, starting at one side and working across to the other. The resulting figure is the same as the one you would get if you strung line across opposite sides of a square frame and then twisted the frame to the skew shape. As before, it is not difficult to imagine a curving surface stretching between the straight lengths of fishline.

Both of these model surfaces are, mathematically speaking, ruled surfaces. A ruled surface is one which can be formed by a moving straight line. In both our models, beautiful curving surfaces are obtained, and yet each consists of a set of straight lines. Two simpler but less elegant ruled surfaces are the cylinder and the cone. In each case, a ruler placed against the surface will touch everywhere along the ruler's edge.

In the case of the one-sheeted hyperboloid, the same surface could have been formed by a running line slanted in the opposite direction. In fact, both sets of lines could be strung on the same frame. Thus two straight lines, not one, pass through each point on the surface. You can try this if you wish, but the

49

resulting figure is somewhat less attractive.

Can you find a second set of lines that will form the hyperbolic paraboloid?

If lines were to be formed between the two remaining edges of the twisted square frame, the same hyperbolic paraboloid surface would be obtained. Again nothing new is added, but each point on this surface also has two straight lines running through it.

Suspend your models, using fine thread. In this way you will be able to see both from every angle. Each view presents a new and fascinating silhouette.

# 12  SEESAW MOBILE

ART, ENGINEERING, and science all utilize mathematics. A fine painting, a bridge, a crystal—all these express mathematical relationships.

Let's design a mobile similar to the one shown in Figure 18. The project will require a little mathematics, some engineering, and the science of the seesaw.

A seesaw is a special kind of lever. If you've ever had any experience with a seesaw, you will remember that you must sit close to the end of the board if you want to balance a person heavier than yourself. If you are heavier than the friend at the other end of the board, you must sit closer to the middle than he does. By adjusting your position you can reduce the tendency of the seesaw to tip one way or the other. You achieve balance.

If you suspend a lightweight stick from a thread tied at its center and hang unequal weights at the ends, the stick will tend to rotate. Scientists use the word *torque* to refer to the tendency of an object to rotate one way or the other. When the stick is equally balanced, like a seesaw, the torque that would spin it in a clockwise direction equals the torque that would spin it in a counterclockwise direction.

The amount of torque is found by multiplying the weight on the stick by the distance between the weight and the axis about which the stick can rotate. Force (in this case the weight) times distance equals torque. A small force at a large distance can balance a larger force closer to the axis.

Now apply this law to the design of a mobile. The mobile will consist of a number of crossarms suspended from one another by thread. Each crossarm will be balanced by a number of ornamental weights. Each arm in a mobile is nothing more than a kind of seesaw. In order to balance, the sum of all the counterclockwise torques on each arm must equal the sum of all the clockwise torques.

**Figure 18.
First Seesaw Mobile**

Look at the picture of the mobile (Figure 18)

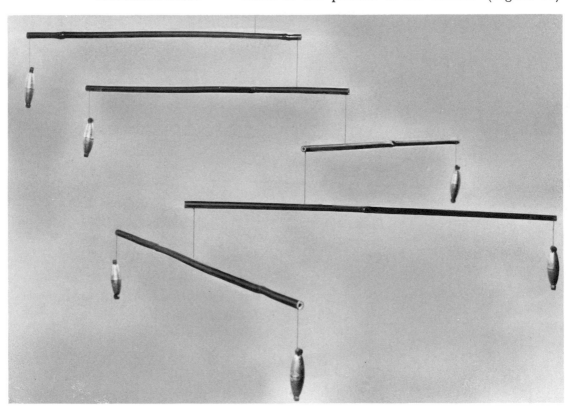

and the drawing that represents it (Figure 19). The five crossarms are balanced by using six identical lead sinkers. Starting with the bottom crossarm, we see that each of the two sinkers is placed at a distance of

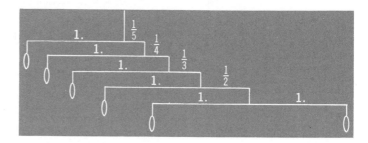

Figure 19.
Design for First Mobile

1 foot from the thread that supports this arm. The point at which this thread is tied is the axis for the bottom crossarm. The right-hand sinker produces a torque that tends to turn the arm in a clockwise direction, while the torque from the left-hand sinker tends to turn the arm in the opposite direction. The two torques are equal since the weight of one sinker times 1 foot equals the weight of the other sinker times 1 foot.

Now look at the arm above. On the left side, one sinker is suspended at a distance of 1 foot from the pivot point for this arm. On the other side, at a distance of ½ foot, the entire bottom arm is suspended, with its two sinkers. If the weight of the arm itself is quite small compared to the weight of the sinkers, the effect on this side is nearly the same as it would be if the two sinkers were hung directly beneath the half-foot mark. The clockwise torque is then the weight of two sinkers times ½ foot. This is the same as the counterclockwise torque produced by the single weight on the left side since $2 \times \frac{1}{2} = 1 \times 1$.

The next-to-the-bottom arm should be in balance. In practice, slight adjustments must be made in the placement of the sinkers to balance out the small weight of the arms.

Look now at the third arm from the bottom. This arm will also balance, since a torque of $3 \times \frac{1}{3}$ equals a torque of $1 \times 1$. For the fourth arm, the clockwise and counterclockwise torques are $4 \times \frac{1}{4}$ and $1 \times 1$. And, finally, for the top arm, $5 \times \frac{1}{5} = 1 \times 1$.

In constructing this mobile, the actual size of the weights makes no difference. It is important only that all six weights be the same. As for the distances, there is no magic in the 1 foot and its fractions used in the example. The 1 foot distance could be replaced by 2 feet, by 6″, or by any other distance. It is important only that the fractions mentioned be fractions of one set distance.

Now look at the somewhat more complicated mobile shown in Figure 20. This mobile has large metal washers for weights. Starting the analysis with the lowest arm, we see that the torques are equal and opposite, since the torque produced by each of the two end weights is the weight of one washer times 1.

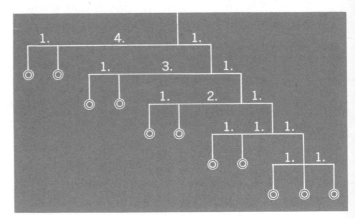

Figure 20.
Design for Second Mobile

The washer in the middle produces no torque. For the next arm above, there are two counterclockwise torques, $1 \times 2$ and $1 \times 1$. This balances the clockwise torque produced by the three washers below on the right, acting at a distance of one unit. Now complete the analysis for the remaining arms.

It will be challenging to design a mobile of your own. There's no limit to the number of different kinds you can design. It is better to use arms made of light material and weights that are relatively heavy. Small-diameter hardwood dowels or bamboo garden stakes make excellent arms. Weights should be chosen for their artistic appeal. Remember that weights may be suspended at any distance below the arms because this distance in no way influences the torque. Cement the supporting threads or strings in place on each arm only after all final adjustments have been made.

It is wise to sketch your design on paper before beginning construction of a mobile. The work will require your artistic, scientific, engineering, and mathematical talents. Place the mobile on display when you have finished so that all may see your suspended series of seesaws in the air.

# 13 TRACING TRICKS

Perhaps you are familiar with the problem of trying to draw a figure with a continuous pencil stroke, without retracing the pencil's path and without lifting the pencil from the paper. Perhaps you do not realize that such problems belong to the branch of mathematics called topology.

Topology has been called rubber-sheet geometry. A figure drawn on a rubber sheet can be twisted, stretched, and distorted as much as you please, and the topological properties remain unchanged. The familiar properties of size and shape are not topological. Since a square can be stretched into a circle and a circle into a triangle, all three shapes are the same topologically. A figure eight is something different, however, because it cannot be stretched or twisted to make a circle. We cannot allow the rubber sheet to be cut and glued, nor folded and overlapped.

Let's make a topologically intricate figure. Instead of drawing it with a single stroke of the pencil, you will trace it with a length of thread. If you can construct the figure without passing along a path more than once, you will obey the rule that corresponds to the one above for figures drawn with a pencil.

Figure 21 shows the figure we will make. The thread has been wound around twenty-one nails spaced evenly along the circumference of an embroidery hoop. This figure is a polygon with twenty-one sides, with lines showing all possible diagonals. (A diagonal is a line connecting any two nonadjacent vertices.) In other words, each nail has been connected only once by thread to each of the other nails.

The important topological question is whether this figure can be constructed from a *single* thread. The answer is Yes. Why not try it and see for yourself? Either use an embroidery hoop, or pound nails in a circle on a board. Take care to space them along the circle evenly for the most attractive results.

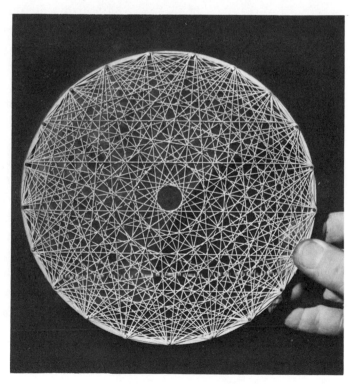

Figure 21.
The Completed
Twenty-one-Sided Polygon

When the nails are in place, tie the thread (better start with a full spool) to one of the nails. Run the thread in a clockwise direction around the nails, first extending the thread around the adjacent nail on the clockwise side. Skip one nail and pass the thread around the next nail, then skip two nails, then three, four, five, six, seven, eight, and finally nine nails. Now repeat the procedure, putting the thread around the nail adjacent to the clockwise side of the last nail. Then skip a nail, then two, and so on until you have skipped nine nails again. Follow this procedure twenty-one times, and not a single diagonal nor any of the twenty-one sides of the figure will have been missed.

Although this intricate figure can be made with a single length of thread, some very simple figures cannot. Examine each of the six figures in Figure 22. The first is a pentagon with an inscribed five-pointed star. It can be drawn without retracing a line. Try to construct each of the six figures. Which can and which cannot be drawn according to the rules? A mathematician would not be content to answer this question for only the six figures shown. He would look for a rule that would determine whether *any* line-figure could be drawn in the prescribed way.

Can you find the rule? Here is a hint. In any figure the point where lines meet or intersect is called a vertex. The vertex can be even (E) or odd (O), according to the even or odd number of lines that are joined. The number of even and odd vertices in a figure is a topological property because this number does not change when the surface of the figure is stretched or twisted.

In each of the six figures, do *not* count the vertices

which are formed simply by the intersection of two straight lines. How many even vertices does each figure have? How many odd?

Any line-figure can be drawn or strung without retracing a line if it has no more than two odd vertices. Our twenty-one-sided figure has only even vertices. Twenty lines meet at each nail.

Figure 22a can also be drawn since all its vertices are even. Figures 22b, c, and f can be drawn too, but Figures 22d and e cannot. Figure 22f is interesting because it cannot be drawn if you start at the wrong point. Try other figures. Does the rule still work?

**Figure 22.
Other Figures To Try**

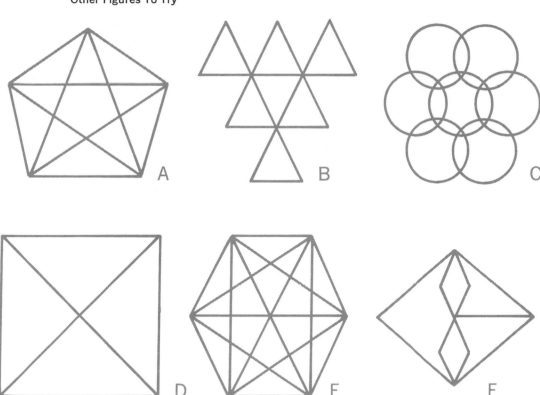

Figure 23 illustrates the problem of the Königsberg bridges. Königsberg is a city in northeast Germany. Seven bridges connect its riverbanks and the two islands in the river. As the story goes, the local residents had long attempted to take an afternoon walk that would take them across each of the seven bridges once and only once. A Swiss mathematician by the name of Euler (pronounced "oiler") was the first to tell them that this was impossible. Euler was the first to find the rule we presented earlier.

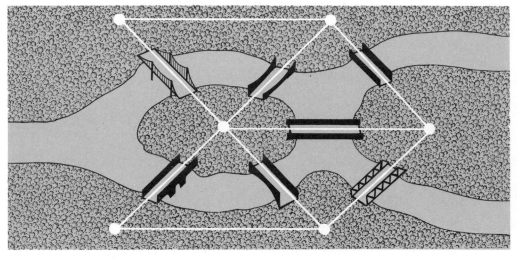

Figure 23.
Königsberg Bridge Problem

Euler also learned the following. A line-figure similar to those shown in Figure 22 (but with no loose ends like those in the letter *A*) cannot have an odd number of odd vertices. A figure that has no odd vertices can be traced from any starting point. A figure with two odd vertices can be traced by starting at one odd vertex and ending at the other.

Could you help the people of Königsberg by building a new bridge? If so, where? By demolishing one of the seven? If so, which one?

# 14 MATHEMATICAL HIEROGLYPHICS

Do THE ACCOMPANYING nine figures seem like some sort of hieroglyphics? Do you suppose they are symbols used in ancient Egyptian or Mayan picture-writing?

The shapes of these figures should be familiar to you, for they represent the twenty-six capital letters of our own alphabet. Mathematicians would say that each capital letter of our alphabet is topologically equivalent to one of the nine hieroglyphs.

Imagine that each letter of our alphabet is elastic. If a letter can be stretched, bent, or compressed (but not folded or cut or glued) so that the resulting figure can be superimposed upon one of the nine figures shown, then these two are said to be topologically equivalent. While a number of our capital letters are topologically equivalent to one another, no two of the nine figures in Figure 24 are topologically the same.

Figure 24.
Topological Equivalents to Our
Twenty-six Capital Letters

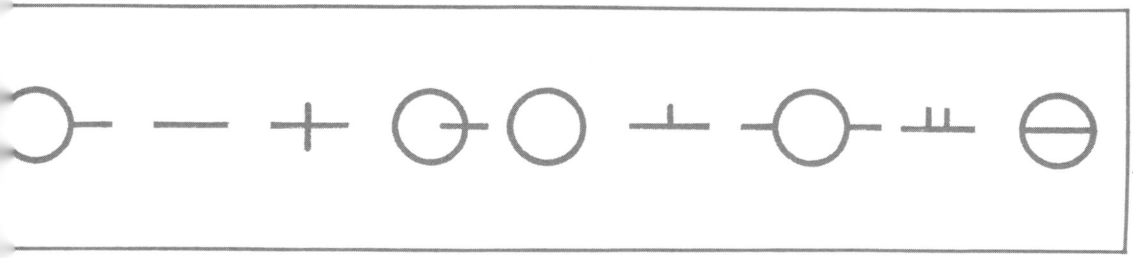

Now test yourself. Find the capital letters that are topologically equivalent to each of the nine hieroglyphs. Use the alphabet shown in Figure 25 for reference. If several letters are equivalent to one of the hieroglyphs, then they are topologically equivalent to one another.

# A B C D E F G H I J K L M N O P Q R S T U V W X Y Z

Do you find that four of the nine hieroglyphs each have only one topologically equivalent capital letter? For three of the figures there are only two equivalent letters, for one figure there are four equivalent letters, and finally for one figure there are twelve topologically equivalent letters.

Our capital-letter alphabet contains twenty-six letters. Topologically, however, there are only nine. Perhaps we should try to construct a twenty-six letter alphabet in which each letter is topologically different.

The concept of topological equivalence may seem abstract and unrelated to everyday problems. It will seem even more abstract in three-dimensional situations than it has in the two-dimensional forms already discussed. In three dimensions, a sphere is topologically equivalent to a cube but not to a doughnut.

Topological problems do arise in the practical world, and in some surprising situations. Consider the problem of printing electronic circuits. To print a circuit means to deposit electrically conducting paths upon an insulating surface. These paths take the place of the wires used in ordinary circuits. Ordinary wires can pass over or under other wires because of the insulation surrounding them. But printed paths that cross one another make an electrical connection. As a result, some circuits can be printed on a single sheet, with each path going around paths to which it must not connect, while other circuits cannot.

Another example arises in highway design. A freeway interchange is quite different topologically from a country crossroad. Divided highways, overpasses, and cloverleaf turns isolate lanes of traffic from one another and so act much like the insulation around current-carrying wires. A freeway interchange cannot be "printed" on a single surface; it may require two or even three different levels for traffic.

# PART FIVE  Mappings and Transformations

## 15  MAPPING:
## MERCATOR, CONIC, AND POLAR

MAPS ARE WONDERFUL things. They show many far-away places and the routes you must follow to travel there. But did you ever stop to wonder how **maps** are made?

The earth is approximately spherical in shape, but maps must be drawn on flat pieces of paper. No matter how hard you try, you simply can't make a spherical surface lie flat. To see that this is so, take the peel of an entire orange and try cutting it so it will lie flat. A small section of orange peel can be made nearly flat, but you will see that a large section would have to be stretched or compressed in places. The problem of the map-maker is to do what cannot be done with an orange peel—to represent the spherical surface of the earth on a two-dimensional map or chart.

A small metal globe of the earth can be made into an excellent device for showing how certain types of maps are made to represent the curved surface of the earth.

Such globes, about 6″ in diameter or even smaller, can be bought at many toy and variety stores for less than a dollar. Make pinholes outlining the continents and use the instructions that follow to mount a flashlight bulb inside the globe. When a paper cylinder, cone, or flat sheet is placed next to the globe, the dots of light shining through the holes form an outline map on the paper. Cylinders and cones make perfectly good maps once they are cut because such surfaces can be made to lie perfectly flat.

It is easy to make small holes in the metal globe with a pushpin because it has a solid aluminum head for easy handling. Punch holes along the outlines of the continents by tapping the pin lightly with a small hammer. Space the holes evenly, about $\frac{1}{8}''$ apart.

Enlarge the hole at the base of the globe to a $\frac{3}{8}''$ or $\frac{1}{2}''$ diameter to allow for the insertion of the flashlight bulb and socket. Sockets for such bulbs may be obtained from a radio supply store or a radio and television repairman. (The correct bulb will depend on whether you use one flashlight battery or two.) Now place the flashlight bulb and socket so the filament of the bulb is at the very center of the globe. Use a long toggle bolt, which has threads along its entire length, as a mounting rod for the socket. You will need two nuts to mount the socket, two nuts with oversized washers to clamp the toggle bolt to the bottom of the globe, and two nuts to mount the bolt to the base of the globe. As an alternative, you can use electrical tape to attach the socket near the end of the toggle bolt. Connect two bell-wire leads to the terminals on the socket and run these wires out through the small hole that you drilled in the South Pole to connect the bulb with the flashlight battery.

The mounting of the bulb will require some care. At this time, final adjustment of the position of the socket should be made in order to locate the bulb filament at the center of the globe. Once this has been done, connect the wires to the battery and darken

Figure 26.
Mercator Projection

the room. The many dots of light that will appear on the walls and ceiling make a beautiful sight.

Now for the map-making. White typing paper is suitable for use as a screen on which to project the dots of light. The light pattern must show clearly through the paper.

Wrap a cylinder of paper around the globe so that it touches only at the equator. The points of light falling upon the cylinder, as shown in Figure 26, make a map of a type you have often seen. It is called a Mercator projection. At the equator the map gives an accurate representation of the outlines on the globe, but as the distance from the equator increases, the outlines of the continents become increasingly distorted. The northernmost lands are greatly oversized.

A second type of map is the conic projection which, as the name implies, is a map projected upon a cone. To make a sufficiently large cone for a 6″ globe, tape two sheets of typing paper together to form a sheet nearly 17″ wide and 11″ high. Draw an arc that forms about five-eighths of a complete circle, using a radius as large as the size of the paper allows. Using the same center, draw another arc with a radius of an inch or two. Now draw two straight lines outward from the center point to connect the extremes of these two arcs, and cut out the complete figure. Join the two straight sides with cellophane tape. When this cone is placed upon the globe, as shown in Figure 27, one parallel of latitude on the globe touches the cone in a complete circle. Distortion of the globe's features is least near this parallel but increases both to the north and south.

Finally, place a flat piece of paper directly on top

**Figure 27.**
**Conic Projection**

of the globe, touching the globe at the North Pole. The resulting map is called a polar projection and is very useful in representing the polar regions.

Straight-line beams of light are used to produce each of the three kinds of maps. A map-maker, of course, uses more accurate techniques, but these are equivalent to the methods used here. Either way, each point on the surface of the earth is represented by one and only one point on the map. Each map is a projection, since each point on the map has been literally projected from its corresponding point on the surface of the earth.

# 16 OPTICAL TRANSFORMER

HERE'S A MAPPING TRICK you won't believe until you see it yourself. It involves two kinds of graphs and the peculiar properties of a cylindrical mirror. Starting with a figure drawn on a sheet of ordinary graph paper, you will first make a very special map that will stretch and twist the figure until it is distorted nearly beyond recognition. A special cylindrical mirror placed near the distorted map will then transform the figure back into its original shape. One such transformation is shown in Figure 28.

To perform this bit of magic you will need several sheets of ordinary (rectangular coordinate) graph paper and several more sheets of polar graph paper. Polar graph paper consists of evenly spaced concentric circles crossed by a set of lines extending from the center of the circles like the spokes of a wheel. In addition, you must obtain a cylindrical mirror. This isn't as difficult as you might think. A section of chrome-plated tubing of the kind used to connect plumbing fixtures (such as a slip extension or tailpiece) will serve as an excellent mirror. This can be obtained from a hardware or building supply store. Select a shiny section, 5" or 6" long with a diameter of 1" or more. This should cost no more than a dollar.

First use a semicircular half of a piece of polar

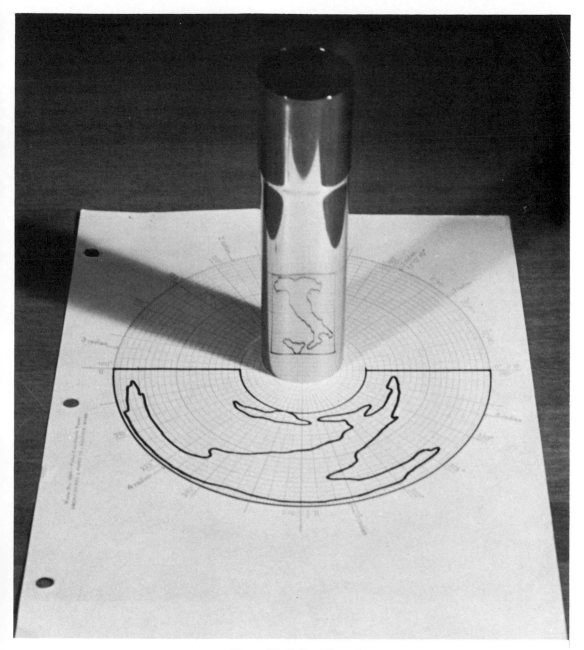

Figure 28. Optical Transformer

69

graph paper. Count the number of spaces between the spokes in a half-circle, then the number of spaces between the smallest and largest concentric circles. Mark off the same number of horizontal and vertical spaces respectively on a corresponding portion of the rectangular graph paper. Figures 29a and 29b

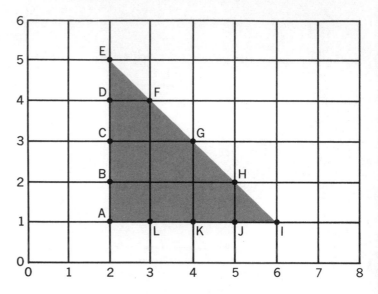

Figures 29a and 29b. Transforming a Triangle

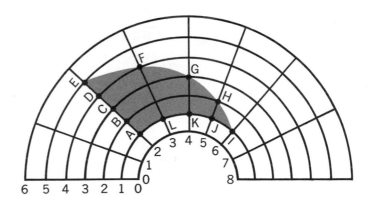

illustrate how the section of polar graph paper can be thought of as the stretched and twisted version of the corresponding portion of the regular graph paper. There are eight "horizontal" spaces and six "vertical" spaces on the polar graph paper that correspond to those on the rectangular graph paper.

Now you are ready to draw a figure on the selected section of rectangular graph paper. Once drawn, this figure can be mapped, point for point, onto the polar graph paper. Point A of the triangle on the rectangular graph, for example, is located two spaces to the right and one space up. The corresponding point on the polar graph, also labeled as point A, is two spaces clockwise and one space outward, as shown. In this way the entire triangle on the first graph is mapped into the distorted figure shown on the polar graph. This distortion is called a map of the figure because each and every point on the map corresponds to one and only one point on the original figure. As you will recall, exactly the same definition of a map was used in the previous chapter.

Now place the cylindrical mirror slightly behind the center of the polar paper at a point that will make the radial and concentric lines of the polar paper appear vertical and horizontal when viewed in the mirror. In the reflection you will see a nice straight-sided triangle! The cylindrical mirror transforms the map back to the shape of the figure from which that map was made. For this reason we call the mirror an optical transformer.

Now try a figure that is more interesting than the simple triangle. Figure 30 shows an outline map of Italy. The map was traced on rectangular graph paper. Then the figure was mapped on polar graph

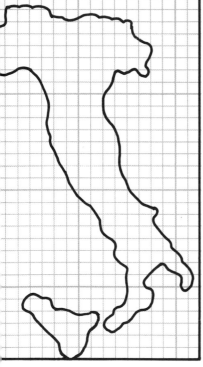

Figure 30. Graph of Italy

paper, as shown in Figure 28. For an irregular figure such as this, a fairly large number of individual points must be mapped and a smooth curve drawn between points. As you see in Figure 28, the polar map of Italy looks more like an abstract drawing than anything else. The image produced by the chrome tubing, however, shows the familiar boot shape in its proper proportions.

You will want to trace different figures, make their polar maps, and see how they are transformed back to their original shapes by the mirror.

# 17 FLEX YOUR BRAIN WITH A FLEXAGON

Figure 31. Flexatube

THE MANIPULATION OF flexagons is one of the most intriguing activities in the entire field of recreational mathematics. Flexagons are figures made of a number of surfaces which can be folded, or flexed, into many forms to bring different surfaces into view. They can be made in a variety of forms—tetraflexagons, hexaflexagons, and many others.

One of the simplest and most interesting members of the flexagon family is the flexatube, shown in Figure 31. When constructed, it takes the form of a cube with the top and bottom surfaces missing. Each of the four square faces can be folded along the two diagonals. A flexagon made of heavy paper should be prefolded along the two diagonals on each of the four faces before it is pasted together to form the cubic box, or tube. The dash lines in Figure 32 indicate the folds. To see how the flexagon works,

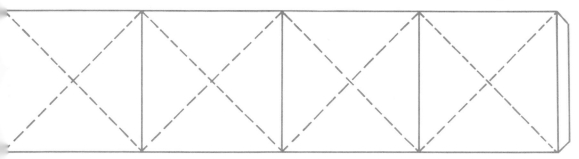

Figure 32. Construction of the Flexatube

make a sturdy model like the one shown in Figure 31. Each face consists of four separate triangular pieces of poster board taped together on both sides to form a square. The four squares are taped together to form a tube. The model flexes easily along these taped edges if the poster-board edges are separated by a distance about three times the thickness of the cardboard.

Construct your own flexagon and flex it yourself to appreciate fully the large variety of shapes it can take. Perhaps the most interesting feature of the flexa-tube is that it can be turned completely inside out. This process may be thought of as a transformation, or mapping, of the tube into its inside-out configuration. If you color or mark the inside faces of the tube, you will be better able to follow your progress in this maneuver. You may wish to try turning the tube inside out on your own before reading the directions that follow.

Start with the flexagon in the form of a cube with the top and bottom open and one of the vertical edges facing you. Now bring the right- and left-upper corners together and, at the bottom, bring together the front- and rear-lower corners to form the flat square shown in Figure 33. Now fold the upper triangular half of this square toward you and against the lower triangular half to make the triangular form shown in Figure 34.

Inside this triangle you will see two loose triangular flaps. Bring the left and right corners of the large triangle together, at the same time making sure that one of these interior flaps folds forward and the other folds to the rear.

Now you will have the small flat square shape

Figure 33.
To turn the flexagon inside out,
first make a square . . .

Figure 34.
then a triangle . . .

75

shown in Figure 35. Examination shows that there are two folded pockets. A triangular pocket appears at the top of the front square, while on the rear of the square the pocket appears at the bottom. Grasp one pocket with the fingers of one hand, the second pocket with the other hand. Pull both these pockets out from the figure and fold the two sides of each pocket together, at the same time giving one pocket a half twist to make a small flat rectangle of the entire flexagon.

Figure 35.
then a smaller square . . .

As you open out this flat rectangle, you will see that you have formed a tube just half the height of the original, as shown in Figure 36. At this point, just half the original tube has been turned inside out, and you can begin the remainder of the operation.

Take the two shorter edges of this rectangle and

Figure 36.
then a half-size tube.

bring them together to form a similar flat rectangle with new right- and left-hand edges.

Now you will perform every previous step in reverse order. Look down into the new rectangle from the direction that shows a double flap on the side of the rectangle away from you and another on the side nearest you. Twist the two ends of the rectangle to move the inside members of these double flaps together and the outside members apart. Keep twisting until the outside pair join back-to-back and the double square is formed that has a pocket in each face. Both sides of this square should be the color that was inside the flexagon when you began. One corner of this square will open so that the corners of the square divide and become the base of a large triangle. The square corners of this triangle fold out to make a larger square. This square, in turn, can be folded out to form a large open cube, the outside faces of which were originally on the inside. The transformation is now complete.

There are other ways to fold the flexagon, and you may wish to color or decorate the faces to exhibit the interesting designs you can make. Be sure that original inside faces of the cube contrast with the outside faces.

# 18 TYSOIZBYJOXS—
## CAN YOU BREAK THIS CODE?

QTLHR THLQZ YBJRL FHUTZ KKZRQ HRQHL IUHJV QELIX IXHZY UHYVL
RHQQE HCLRU LRIXH EZYVU LIOYZ THHUQ CYZKI XHJQQ DKOIL ZRIXJ
IIXHO XHRZK HRJEX LTXLK OLRBH ZRZDY QHRQH QJYHQ DWPHT IIZYD
VHWSV JEJRU LIXJQ JQLIQ JLKIX HULQT ZAHYS ZCIXJ IWZUS ZCVJE

SECRET MESSAGES ARE a lot of fun. They're serious business, however, for our Central Intelligence Agency and for our armed forces.

Although there are thousands of ways to write coded messages, or ciphers, only two basic methods are the foundation of them all. A cipher may be formed by transposition, by substitution, or by a combination of these two methods.

In a transposition cipher, the normal order of the symbols or letters that compose the message is changed. A word spelled backward or scrambled in some way is one type of transposition cipher.

In a substitution cipher, the letters in the words of the message retain their normal order, but each original letter is represented by an entirely different symbol or letter. For example, *QKZ* might represent the word *THE* if, everywhere in the message, *Q* is substituted for *T*, *K* for *H*, and *Z* for *E*.

Every coded message contains letters or other symbols obtained by making a prescribed transformation of the letters in the original message. To decode a message you must determine what transformation has been made.

Suppose you have a substitution cipher you wish to analyze. Suppose also that the letters used as substitutes have been selected entirely at random. How would you break the cipher? How would you begin?

A message of this type can be deciphered by using a mathematical analysis. You first must know the probability for the occurrence of each letter in the alphabet. The letter *E*, for example, occurs far more frequently than any other letter in normal written English. In fact, it occurs about 12.7 percent of the time. The least-used letter is *Z*. On the average, it appears about once in every thousand letters.

The table below gives the probability for each letter in the alphabet, expressed as a percentage. The data was obtained through the examination of a very large amount of written material.

| | | | |
|---|---|---|---|
| E — | 12.7 | F — | 2.6 |
| T — | 9.3 | M — | 2.4 |
| O — | 8.1 | P — | 2.2 |
| A — | 7.9 | W — | 1.8 |
| N — | 7.2 | Y — | 1.7 |
| I — | 7.0 | G — | 1.5 |
| S — | 6.5 | B — | 1.4 |
| R — | 6.3 | V — | 1.0 |
| H — | 5.5 | K — | 0.5 |
| D — | 3.9 | X — | 0.2 |
| L — | 3.8 | Q — | 0.2 |
| C — | 3.1 | J — | 0.2 |
| U — | 2.9 | Z — | 0.1 |

Now let's try to decipher the message at the beginning of this chapter.

Cryptograms are ordinarily written in groups of five letters so that the length of each word in the message is completely obscured.

The first step consists of counting the number of occurrences of each letter in the message. List the letters in decreasing order of their number of appearances. The letter *H* heads the list since it appears twenty-five times in all. *Q* is next, appearing eighteen times, *I* and *L* follow with seventeen each, and so on. Since there are exactly two hundred letters in the message, the percentage of occurrence of each of these letters is obtained simply by dividing the number of times each appears by two:

$$\text{percentage of occurrence} = \frac{\text{number of times used}}{200} \times 100$$

Write the percentage of occurrence following each of the letters.

Now you can compare the occurrence of the various letters in the message with the expected occurrence given in the preceding table. You can't expect the precise order to be the same, but you can narrow the possibilities considerably.

Inspection of the table shows that the letter *H* in the message has undoubtedly been substituted for the letter *E*. *H* appears 12.5 percent of the time in the message, whereas the expected rate of occurrence of the letter *E* is 12.7 percent. This looks almost too good to be true.

Copy the message on a separate sheet of paper and write an *E* above each of the twenty-five *H*'s that occur. After *E*, the next most popular letter in written

English is *T*. In the message *Q* appears eighteen times. Try this substitution by writing *T* above each of the eighteen *Q*'s. Note that only one *T__E* combination appears in the spaces above the message. It would be rather unusual to find the word *THE* only once in a message of this length.

Because of this, *Q* may not be the correct substitute for *T* in this message. Try the next most frequent letter in the message. There are two that appear seventeen times. These are *I* and *L*. First try *I* as a substitute for *T*. When this is done, *T__E* appears above the message not once, but six times. In five of these six cases the letter combination in the message is *IXH*, so it would seem that *IXH* in the cipher stands for *THE*. *X* is the substitute for *H*, and *I* is the correct substitute for *T*.

Now look for other places where you have written the two-letter *TH* combination in addition to its appearance in the word *THE*. Notice that there are two instances of *TH__T*. In both these cases the message letter in the blank spot is the same. This certainly looks like it might be the word *THAT*, and if so, *J* must be the substitute for *A*.

We are left with the medium-popular letters *O*, *N*, *I*, *S*, and *R* to identify. According to our table, these are very likely represented by *Z*, *R*, *L*, *Q*, and *Y*, but not necessarily in this order.

Two other *TH* combinations remain unidentified. In one of these situations, it is possible that the *T* ends one word while the *H* begins another. In the other instance, however, *TH* must end a word because the word *THE* immediately follows. Try to think of a fairly common word that ends in *TH*. Quite possibly it's the word *WITH*. From now on, you're on your own. The remainder of the message should not be particularly difficult. When you're finished, but not before, check your results with the alphabet and its substitutes given below. The message itself, of course, should make good sense.

With this code you can also decipher the title of this chapter. Develop your own substitution cipher if you wish and try it on your friends. Then have one of them send a message for you to decipher.

| Real Letter | Coded Letter | Real Letter | Coded Letter |
|---|---|---|---|
| A | J | N | R |
| B | W | O | Z |
| C | T | P | O |
| D | U | Q | G |
| E | H | R | Y |
| F | C | S | Q |
| G | B | T | I |
| H | X | U | D |
| I | L | V | A |
| J | P | W | E |
| K | M | X | N |
| L | V | Y | S |
| M | K | Z | F |

# PART SIX Soap-Film Mathematics

## 19  SOAP CIRCLES

EVERYONE AT ONE TIME or another has blown soap bubbles. But have you ever made soap circles? If not, you're in for a surprise. Soap circles can be as fascinating as soap bubbles.

You will need a small wire frame, some thread, and a little soap-bubble solution. If you obtain about 10 feet of soft brass wire, $\frac{1}{16}''$ in diameter, you will have enough to make the wire frames described in Chapter 21. The soap solution can be bought at any toy counter or made from true soap—not detergent.

Bend the soft wire into a square frame 2" on a side and extend a short length of wire from the square to serve as a handle. Now make a loop of thread that is smaller than the width of the frame. Attach the loop to two opposite sides of the frame with short lengths of thread, allowing a little slack when making these connections.

When you dip the frame into the soap-bubble solution, a soap film will form across the entire area of the frame. Now puncture the film inside the loop of thread. Presto! The loop of thread will immediately form a circle like the one shown in Figure 37.

Try it again. The loop of thread once more forms a circle. Why is the circle formed? Why not a triangle, a square, or even a pentagon?

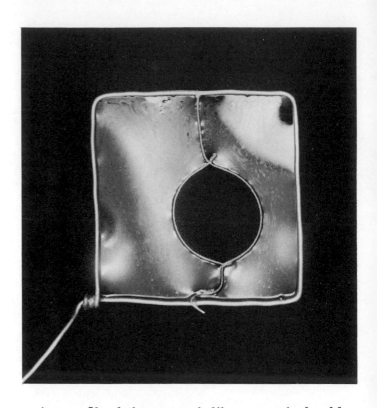

Figure 37. Soap Circle

A soap film behaves much like a stretched rubber membrane. It is stretched with equal tension everywhere and pulls in all directions along the surface of the film. When the film inside the loop is broken, the film outside pulls equally in all directions. It tends to make its own area as small as possible. This makes the area inside the loop of thread as large as it can possibly be, given the limit of the length of the thread in the loop. The result is that the loop assumes the shape which gives it the maximum area for the perimeter to which it is limited. This figure is always a circle. There is another way to state this relationship: A circle has the least possible perimeter for a given area.

Perhaps now you can guess why soap bubbles are spherical in shape rather than cubical or pyramidal. Spheres have the greatest possible volume for a given surface area. To put it another way, they have the least possible surface area for a specified volume.

Circles and spheres have other very special properties. A circle is the most symmetric figure that can be drawn on a flat surface. From the center outward it is the same in all directions. And if you cut a circle straight through its center, each half is the mirror image of the other half, no matter what direction the figure is sliced. Similarly, a sphere is the most symmetric three-dimensional figure.

Before putting your soap-circle frame on the shelf, try using it to make some abstract art. Remove the loop of string and tie about ten lengths of thread across the frame in all directions, allowing some slack in each thread. After dipping the frame in the soap solution, break the film in various places between the threads. Some very artistic results can be achieved with a little practice.

# 20 DOUBLE BUBBLE

SCIENTIFIC EXPERIMENTS which seem to have no practical importance are often the most fascinating of all. There is always a bit of knowledge to be gained that might eventually prove useful.

Such is the case with the double-bubble experiment. Let's construct a simple but specialized kind of soap-bubble pipe, consisting of a short hollow cylinder with a small blowing tube inserted in the side. The spool inside a roll of adhesive tape will serve well as the cylinder, or a cardboard tube may be used if it is first coated with waterproof cement. The blowing pipe may be a soda straw, a short length of bamboo, or some other small tube. Make your own soap-bubble solution or obtain the kind sold at any toy counter.

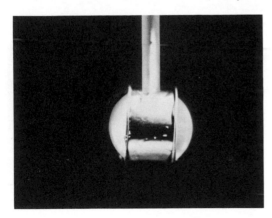

Figure 38. Blow Gently

Figure 39. Two Hemispheres Form

The idea is to blow two bubbles with the pipe, one from each end of the open cylinder. To start the bubbles, dip each end of the cylinder into the solution. If you lose your soap-film at one end of the cylinder as you turn the pipe over to immerse the other end, then form a second film by drawing a finger moistened with the solution across the end of the cylinder.

Now gently blow through the pipe. Two identical bubbles will begin to form. Continue blowing slowly. The two bubbles will continue to grow until they become hemispheres. At this point something very peculiar will happen. One bubble will continue to increase in size while the other becomes smaller and smaller.

Try it again. Make sure that this wasn't a freak performance. Try as you may, it is impossible to blow two large bubbles of equal size with your pipe. It is also impossible to predict which side of your pipe will form the large bubble and which will form the shrinking bubble.

There must be a logical explanation for this be-

Figure 40. One Bubble Becomes Larger

Figure 41. The Other Bubble Becomes Smaller

havior. Recall that a soap bubble behaves as if it were a stretched rubber membrane. Because of this, as we saw in the previous chapter, a soap bubble is spherical, enclosing the maximum amount of air while using the least possible soap-film area.

In this experiment, however, we have the complication of two bubbles. In reality, the two bubbles are one since they enclose a single volume of confined air. They are simply two different surfaces of a single bubble. The bubble tends to form a sphere, but it can't alter the shape of the air enclosed by the cylinder. In spite of the presence of the rigid cylinder, the bubble forms two sections of a single sphere, part on one side of the pipe and the remainder on the other.

Blow the pipe once more and check the shape of the small bubble compared to the large. If the small bubble section were placed on the missing part of the larger bubble, it would almost exactly fill the space. The curious behavior of the two sections of the bubble, once the hemispheres are formed, is not so curious after all. The bubble sections form the least possible surface area to cover the enclosed air.

With this experiment in mind, it is simple to analyze a thought-experiment. Imagine that two nearly identical bubbles were blown with two separate pipes. Now mentally connect the two pipe chambers to form a passageway for air from one bubble to another. What happens? Since it is impossible to form two bubbles that are exactly the same size, one bubble must be a little larger than the other. The larger bubble will grow at the expense of the smaller until two sections of a single sphere are formed.

# 21 THESE ARE SOAP BUBBLES?

SOAP BUBBLES AND soap films are as interesting as they are beautiful. We have already seen that a circle is the shape with the greatest area for a given perimeter and that a sphere is the shape with the least surface area for a fixed volume. Soap films, however, can be made to solve problems of minimum surface area far more complicated than those of the circle and the sphere. Many soap-film answers will be both strange and beautiful.

You will need about 10 feet of soft brass wire, to make frames, and some soap solution. The wire should be nearly $1/16''$ in diameter; a thinner wire may be used if it is fairly rigid. The solution must be made from real soap, not detergent, and you should have at least a cupful.

Use pliers to bend the lengths of wire to form the figures and then extend wire from one corner to form a handle. Make the frames small enough so that they can be submerged completely in the cup of soap solution.

Make two circular loops about the size of a quarter from the wire, and connect them by a handle formed from a single length of bent wire. The two wire circles should be set parallel, about a $1/2''$ apart. The handle should be flexible enough to allow the space between the circles to be increased or decreased.

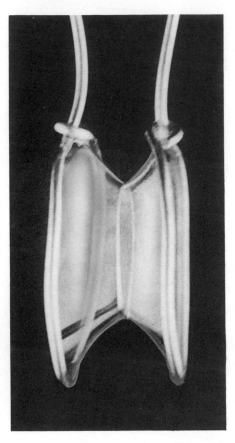

Figure 42.
Film on the Double Circle Frame

Before forming a soap film on this frame, ask yourself this question: What will be the shape of the surface with the least possible area that can connect the two wire circles and form a hollow tube? Don't answer too quickly, for a cylindrical surface is not the right answer.

When you think you have some idea of the proper shape for the minimal surface, dip the frame into your solution. You will have a soap film in three parts, as shown in Figure 42. This is not the answer we're looking for, since this film not only connects the two wire loops but spans them as well. It is, of course, the shape of the surface with the least area that will make this kind of connection. Now puncture the middle, flat film. A surface curved something like an hourglass is formed. This is the surface with the least area that can connect the two circular loops. Is it the shape you had anticipated?

The surface narrows at the center between the loops because the distance around the circular neck in the film becomes smaller and thus reduces the film's area. But the smaller the neck, the greater is the distance along the film from loop to loop. Therefore, the neck cannot become too small without increasing the surface area. And so the shape formed is a compromise in these two lengths, a compromise that gives the surface of minimum area. Notice how the hourglass shape changes when the two wire circles are moved closer and then farther apart.

Now make a triangular pyramid, or regular tetrahedron, from a piece of wire. This figure has four triangular faces: Three triangular sides extend upward to a point with a fourth triangle at the base. Dip the frame into the soap solution, then withdraw it slowly. Figure 43 shows the resultant bubble.

Instead of the four soap-film faces you might expect, a beautiful figure of six films appears. The six films extend inward from each wire to meet at a single point at the center of the frame. This point may also be thought of as the intersection of the four film edges which start at each of the four corners of the wire frame. Each of these soap-film edges is the intersection of three separate films.

This frame illustrates several general rules about soap films. No matter how complicated the wire frame, the greatest number of films that ever join at a single edge is three. In addition, no more than four edges, or six films, ever meet at any one point. Also, the films and edges always meet at equal angles.

The cubical frame in Figure 44 forms an amazingly intricate pattern of films. You will get a network of thirteen flat films. Twelve films extend in toward the center of the frame from the twelve edges of the cube. They cannot all meet at a single point at the center of the cube, for we just learned that the number is limited to six. Therefore, the film forms a thirteenth face at the center in the shape of a square, and the edge of each soap film becomes the intersection of three films, making angles of 120° to one another.

If you happen to trap a bubble inside the cubical frame when you withdraw it from the solution, a

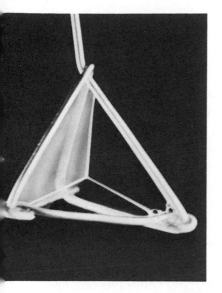

Figure 43.
Film on Pyramidal Frame

Figure 44.
Film on Cubical Frame

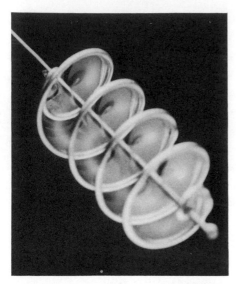

Figure 45.
Helix Frame with Central Wire

Figure 46.
Moebius-Strip Frame

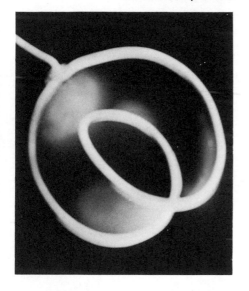

small soap-film cube will form at the center of the frame instead of the flat, square film.

Why do soap films take such odd forms on these frames? It is because the surfaces formed have the minimum total area possible to connect the edges of the frame. The total surface area is always less, for example, than the area of film required to cover the outside faces of the frame.

To form another interesting surface, coil a wire around a broom handle four or five times as shown in Figure 45, leaving ½″ space between turns. This figure is called a helix. Attach both ends of the coil to a straight length of wire that extends down the center of the coil. The screw surface formed by soap film is as beautiful as any you could hope to see.

Finally, a fascinating one-sided Moebius-strip surface can be made from soap solution. A Moebius strip is usually made from a long strip of paper, by gluing the two ends together after a half-twist has been given to one of these ends. To make a soap-film frame for such a strip, form a loop in a short length of wire, then bring the two ends of the wire together in a larger loop and attach a handle as in Figure 46. You may have to bend the wire a little to get the desired film surface. If a film forms across the center of the smaller loop, puncture it. One can "walk" completely over the famous Moebius strip surface without ever going over the edge of the wire frame. There is no front or back to this film; there is only one side.

You may have still other ideas for soap-film frames. Try them. Remember that each film contracts into the least possible area, and in this way it solves a mathematical problem that would be extremely difficult, if not impossible, to solve any other way.

# 22 SOAP-FILM HIGHWAYS

THE STATE ROAD COMMISSION had a difficult problem on its hands. The towns of Xenon, Yardley, and Zimmer (X, Y, and Z for short) had been promised a new road that would connect each of the towns to the other two.

The Commission wanted to find the shortest possible route so as to keep costs at a minimum. The three towns formed a triangle, and a road from Xenon to Yardley and another from Yardley to Zimmer would surely do the job. X would be connected to Z simply by traveling through Y. But the chief of the Road Commission suspected that there might be a shorter connection, and he put his assistants to work on the problem.

Next morning one of the road designers came to work with some soap-bubble solution, two clear plastic sheets, and several small nails. Within a few moments he was able to show the others how soap films could solve their highway problem.

You can solve this and other road-building problems yourself. In addition to the soap solution, you will need a small clear plastic box about 2″ by 3″ in size. Ask your pharmacist if he sells bobby pins or some other inexpensive article that is packed in such boxes. A clear plastic sandwich box can be used.

Saw or file away the sides of the box but not

the hinges and the snap fastener on the front. The object is to leave the top and bottom of the box separated by a fixed distance but to leave the sides open. Drill five very small holes through the top of the box and five more in the bottom of the box, directly beneath the holes above. These should be placed somewhat irregularly along an oval or circular line almost as large as the top of the box. Now insert small finishing nails, or lengths of heavy brass wire, through three of the pairs of holes.

Submerge the entire box in the soap-bubble solution. This will completely wet the inside. Blow out any films that form. Now moisten a flattened soda straw with the solution. With the straw touching two of the nails, move it slowly from the bottom to the top of the box. This will leave a film that extends between the two nails and the top and bottom of the box.

Repeat this procedure to form a film between the third nail and the center of the film already suspended between the first two nails. The soap film will

**Figure 47.**
**Shortest Path Connecting**
**Three Points**

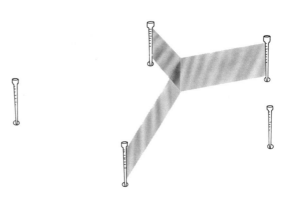

slide into a position that makes three straight films, one from each nail, which meet at a point inside the triangular arrangement of nails. Occasionally films will join to different portions of a nail so that there are only two films where there should be three. When this happens, merely stroke the nail with the moistened straw.

The three nails represent the villages of X, Y, and Z. The lines along which the connecting soap films meet the box represent the path of the shortest possible road connecting the three towns. The stretchy soap film slides freely across the top and bottom of the box and then contracts. It is this property of the soap film that makes its position the right answer to the road-building problem.

Sometimes the shortest road to connect three towns will consist of only two straight stretches of highway. This is true when the triangle formed by the three towns has one angle greater than a third of a full circle, or 120°. If each of the angles is less than 120°, the shortest road system is the kind that has three sections meeting at a point inside the triangle.

This road-building problem can also be solved by using higher mathematics. But the soap films solve the problem accurately, with beauty, and in far less time.

Now imagine a fourth town, and insert another nail in an empty hole, between the top and bottom of the box. To find the shortest possible road connecting all four towns form the soap films between the nails as before. Do the same for a fifth town. Notice particularly that at those points where three soap films meet the angles between the films are always 120°. The soap-film system usually forms a

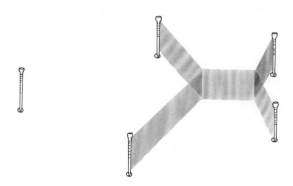

Figure 48. Four Points

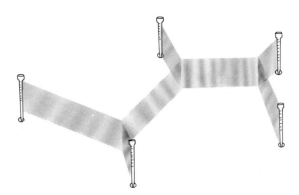

Figure 49. Five Points

kind of honeycomb network connecting the nails.

How is it that these soap films can show the short-test paths connecting several points? Previously we found that soap films form minimal areas, not minimal paths. This is a problem for you to solve.

# PART SEVEN Mathematical Machines

## 23 THE PANTOGRAPH

HAVE YOU EVER NEEDED to make a scale drawing—a traced copy of a map or other figure that is two, three, or four times larger than the original? Or perhaps you have wanted a tracing that is reduced to a half, a third, or a quarter of the original size.

All this is easily done with a simple pantograph made from a wooden yardstick. The pantograph puts elementary geometry to good use. Two similar triangles in the structure of the pantograph maintain a predetermined size-ratio between the original drawing and the copy traced from it.

To make the pantograph you will need an ordinary wooden yardstick of the type available (usually without cost) from a building supply store. You will also need five 1″ roundheaded brass machine screws, size number five, fitted with hex nuts and brass washers. A piece of sandpaper and ⅛″ and ¼″ drills will also be required.

First saw the yardstick in half to make two 18″ lengths. Now saw each of these lengthwise, down the middle, to make a total of four 18″ sections each about ½″ wide. Be careful not to split the stick during these lengthwise cuts. A hacksaw will do the job well. Now stack the four pieces together and sand the sawed edges smooth.

Two pieces of the yardstick will be marked with

the inch scale. Carefully draw a line lengthwise down the center of one of these pieces. Make small indentations on the line at each of the seventeen inch-marks, with a punch or sharp nail. Clamp this piece on top of the stack of four, and drill a ⅛″ hole through the stack at each of the seventeen marks.

Now assemble these sticks into a pantograph following the arrangement shown in Figure 50. The ⅛″

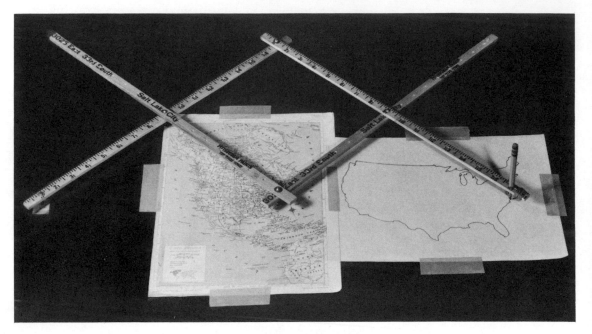

Figure 50. Pantograph

holes are just the right size for your number five machine screws. Insert the screws, place a washer between the arms, and attach the nuts at each of the four places where the arms overlap. The pantograph should now stretch and contract in accordion fashion. The four arms form two overlapping inverted V's, joined together by the screws in the middle of each arm.

The pantograph is supported by the ends of the four screws that extend below the overlapping sticks. Insert the fifth screw at the lower-left end of the upside-down V. Shorten this screw to make the pantograph level and file the end of the screw to a point. This is the one stationary point about which the pantograph will pivot. Then file the screw at the base of the upright V to a point. This will be a pointer to follow the outlines of the figure to be traced. The other three screw ends should be covered with adhesive tape or filed smooth so that they can slide easily over the table.

Enlarge the hole at the lower right of the inverted V to $\frac{1}{4}''$ and make a saw-slot that extends from the end of this arm into the hole. Now fasten a rubber band around the end of the arm to close the saw-slot. A sharpened pencil can be wedged into this hole to keep this side of the pantograph at the proper level.

Place several pieces of adhesive tape under the pointed pivot to protect the tabletop and keep the instrument in position. Use masking tape to keep the material to be traced and the paper for the enlargement in place. The pantograph is now ready to double all dimensions traced by the pointer.

Try a simple drawing first. You should obtain an excellent reproduction which differs from the original only in its dimensions and not at all in its shape.

The pantograph works because of two similar triangles built into the instrument. The three vertices (points where the sides meet) of the smaller triangle are the pivot point, the left intersection of the two pantograph V's, and the pointer. The vertices of the larger triangle are the pivot point, the top of the upside-down pantograph V, and the pencil. Although the shapes of these two triangles change as the pantograph is stretched or compressed, at any one time they both have precisely the same shape. In the two-to-one, or doubling, adjustment, every side of the larger triangle is twice the length of the corresponding side of the smaller triangle.

If the left-hand intersection of the two pantograph V's is moved 12″ from the pivot (to the 13-mark on the scale) and the right-hand intersection of the V's is moved to a point 4″ from the pencil, the ratio of the dimensions of the two triangles becomes 16 to 12, or 4 to 3. This means that each dimension of your tracing will be ⅓ larger than the original. This adjustment is shown in Figure 51.

In another case, if the left-hand intersection is moved to 4″ from the pivot and the right-hand intersection is moved to 12″ from the pencil, as in Figure

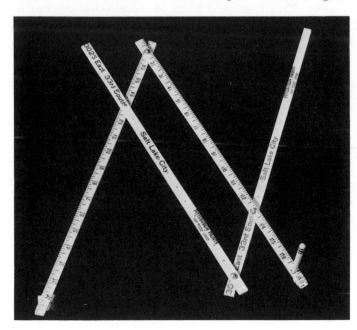

Figure 51.
Enlarging in the Ratio 4:3

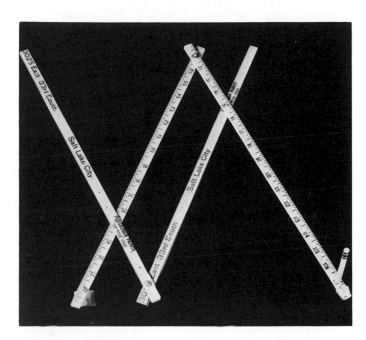

Figure 52.
Enlarging in the Ratio 4:1

52, the enlargement provided by the pantograph will be 16 to 4, or 4 to 1.

For all adjustments of the pantograph, the pivot, pointer, and pencil are kept in a line. In addition, the opposite sides of the four-sided figure formed by the overlapping V's of the pantograph must be kept equal in length so that a parallelogram is formed. With this in mind, any enlargement intermediate to the ones above is easy to obtain.

If you wish to reduce the size of a map or drawing, the position of the movable pointer and that of the pencil must be interchanged. Construct a fifth arm identical to the one holding the pencil. Move the arm with the pencil and the new arm into the position of the upright V, and move one of the arms with the pointer mounted on it to the right side of the inverted V.

101

# 24 THE NOTHING GRINDER

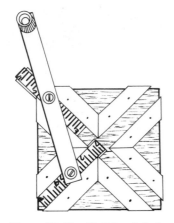

Figure 53. The Nothing Grinder

HAVE YOU EVER HEARD of the nothing grinder? It grinds and grinds away and does absolutely nothing. When the handle of the grinder is turned, its smooth rotary motion is transmitted to two sliders mounted in perpendicular, crossing channels. The sliders move back and forth along straight-line paths, narrowly missing each other four times during each revolution of the crank. Not only do the sliders keep missing each other by the narrowest of margins, but the resulting pair of perpendicular straight-line motions produced by the turning of the crank handle also seem completely out of place.

The nothing grinder is based upon sound mathematical principles. Perhaps you would like to discover the geometry that makes the grinder so fascinating and so workable. You might even discover a way to put this mechanism to a practical use.

Start by building a nothing grinder of your own. The drawings in this chapter show the basic construction and the general motion of the handle and the two sliders. You will need a square wooden block 4½″ on the side, a wooden yardstick, sixteen wire brads ¾″ long, two ⅝″ × 5″ roundheaded wood screws, four small circular felt pads to act as washers, and the cap from a tube of toothpaste. You will also need a hacksaw blade, a small utility saw, a hand drill, sandpaper, a hammer, and epoxy resin.

Use the hacksaw blade to cut the yardstick lengthwise into two 36″ pieces along a line that will make one piece about $\frac{3}{16}$″ wider than the other. Sand the two rough edges of these pieces. Also sand one face of the wider strip lightly so that this piece will have a thickness somewhat less than that of the other strip. Now carefully center the narrow strip on top of the wider strip and glue the pieces together with epoxy resin. This will make a single yard-long strip that has a flange on both edges. Let the resin set overnight. From this special two-layer wooden strip you will construct the channels, the sliders, and the crank arm.

Cut the strip into ten 3″ pieces and a single 6″ piece. Sand the ends of two of the 3″ pieces and those of the 6″ piece and set them aside. These will form the two sliders and the crank handle. The remaining eight pieces will be the channels for the sliders. Make a 45° cut at one end of each of these eight pieces so that they will fit together near the center of the square block, as shown in Figure 53. Four of these must be cut along lines from the upper left to lower right and the other four from upper right to lower left. Don't concern yourself with the square ends for the moment.

Assemble the eight channel pieces on the square wooden base, with the flanges on top. The sliders will, of course, be positioned with the flanges down. Temporarily use the crank arm in one channel and both sliders in the other channel to position these eight pieces accurately. Nail in place the four pieces that surround the crank arm. Now place the crank arm in the cross-channel and nail the remaining four pieces in place. Lightly sand the sliders and the channel pieces as needed to enable the sliders to move freely back and forth. Saw off the outer ends of the eight channel pieces flush with the edge of the square base, then sand these ends smooth.

To attach the crank arm, first locate the center of each slider as accurately as you can and mark the point with a small indentation from a nail. Insert the two sliders, one in each channel, so that one end of each slider is just ¹⁄₁₆″ or less away from the position that would block the motion of the other slider if it were to be moved back and forth. When this is done, the two points marked previously on the sliders will lie on a line parallel to one side of the square

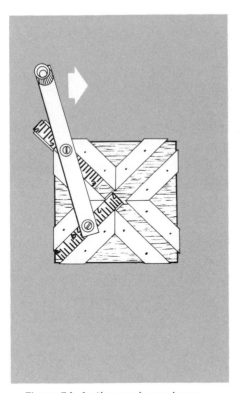

Figure 54. As the crank arm turns . . .

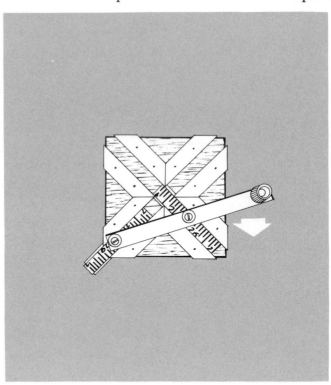

Figure 55. the sliders move . . .

base. Measure the distance between the center points on the sliders. This same distance is now marked between two corresponding points on the crank arm. One of these two points on the arm should be placed at one end. Now drill ⅛″ holes at these two points. The screws should rotate freely in holes of this size. Insert the screws through these holes, using a felt washer on both sides of the crank arm, and screw them into the two center points on the sliders. Finally, use epoxy resin to affix the toothpaste cap at the end of the crank arm to provide a small handle. Your nothing grinder is now complete. Turn the handle and you too can grind for as long as you please.

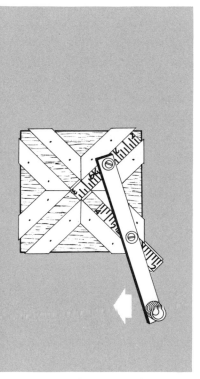

Figure 56. back and forth . . .

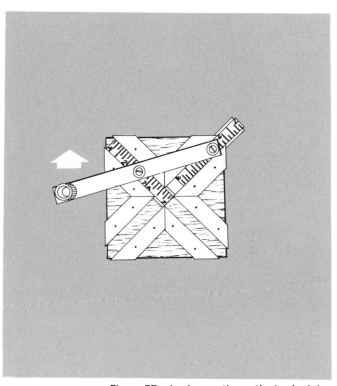

Figure 57. obeying mathematical principles.

Now you are ready to analyze the motion of the grinder. The motion that is easiest to analyze is that of the handle. It executes a smooth oval-shaped motion. One of the channels in the square block is directed along the long dimensions of the oval, and the other channel is directed along the short dimension of the oval.

The oval happens to be a very special curve called an ellipse. An ellipse is a mathematical curve that can be described in any one of a number of different ways. An ellipse is obtained when one slices at an angle through an ice-cream-cone-shaped figure. Depending on the angle of the slice, the ellipse obtained may be fat, almost the shape of a circle, or much more elongated. An ellipse may be drawn around two pins placed a short distance apart by using a closed loop of thread or string of such size that there is some slack when the loop is placed around the pins. A pencil placed inside the loop and pushed outward as far as possible will inscribe a smooth ellipse when the pencil is moved around the pins. The size and shape of the ellipse depends on the size of the loop of string and the distance between the pins. An ellipse may also be described by an algebraic formula. The nothing grinder also provides a way to define and draw an ellipse. All these methods are equivalent, for each provides a way to describe an ellipse. Proving that they are equivalent, however, is a difficult task.

Watch closely the behavior of the grinder. See if you can find a point on the crank arm which moves along a circular path. Other points along the crank arm move along elliptical paths for which the long dimension is oriented at right angles to the long dimension of the ellipse traced by the handle. Can you find these? Notice also that some ellipses are very elongated, while others are short and fat.

And now for the last problem. Can you find a practical use for this linkage? It has been used as a machine for drawing ellipses. Perhaps it may be most useful simply doing nothing—nothing more, that is, than providing good mathematical stimulation.

# 25 A CLEVER YARN

A LENGTH OF YARN can be put to clever use. With it you can solve some extremely difficult mathematical problems. When used on a special computing board, the yarn gives answers quickly and accurately.

Suppose you have three containers, one which will hold 12 quarts, a second which will hold 7 quarts, and a third of 5-quart capacity. Starting with the 12-quart vessel full and the other two empty, can you divide the liquid into two 6-quart portions? None of the vessels should have markings of any kind. You must also use the method that requires the least number of pourings. Yarn and a computing board can be used to solve this problem easily.

A computing board can be constructed from a small piece of lumber and a handful of small nails. A parallelogram approximately $4\frac{1}{2}'' \times 6\frac{1}{2}''$, with $60°$ angles at the lower-left- and upper-right-hand corners and $120°$ angles at the other two corners, is marked on the board.

Draw three sets of lines on the board, spaced $\frac{1}{2}''$ apart. Ten lines should be horizontal, parallel to the top and bottom edges of the parallelogram, and thirteen lines should be parallel to the left- and right-hand edges.

Beginning with the lower-left-hand corner, number the ten horizontal lines 0 to 9 from bottom to top along the left edge. Number the thirteen lines 0 to 12 along the bottom line. The 0 point on both sets of lines should be the same. Now draw twenty lines that make a 60° angle to each of the first two sets of lines and form small equilateral triangles. Drive a nail into the board at every point of intersection of the three sets of lines. Now we are ready to use the yarn to solve the problem mentioned before.

The 12-quart vessel is full, whereas both the 7- and 5-quart vessels are empty. How can the 12 quarts be divided into two equal portions?

Let the horizontal lines (numbered from bottom to top) represent the contents of the 5-quart container, and let the lines parallel to the left and right edges (numbered along the bottom) represent the

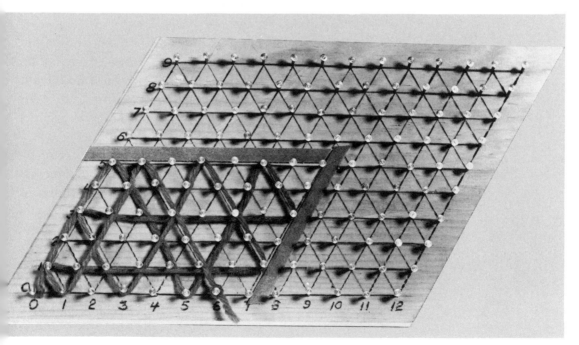

Figure 58. Computer Solution To Obtain Two 6-Quart Portions

109

number of quarts of liquid to be found at any one time in the 7-quart container. Mark the board above the 5 on the horizontal rows of nails and to the right of the 7 at the bottom to outline the smaller parallelogram you will need for this particular problem.

Now tie a length of yarn or thread to the 0,0 nail. This point represents the two smaller vessels, neither of which contains any liquid at the outset. From this point run the yarn up along the left boundary of nails to the number 5 to show that the 5-quart container has been filled. We refer to this as 0,5. The 7-quart container, which is still empty, is the 0 in the pair of numbers and is always written as the first number in the pair. Thus each boundary point on the parallelogram represents the number of quarts of liquid that remain in the two smaller containers after each pouring.

Remember that the 12-quart container is always in use, although it is not shown. Whatever part of the original 12 quarts *not* in the smaller containers at any stage of the pouring *is* in the large one. With every point you plot on the computing board, keep in mind the amount *not* represented.

When the yarn touches a point on the edge of the board, it must reflect as if it were a bouncing ball or a ray of light, and then continue to the next point of reflection at the boundary of the parallelogram. Thus from 0,5 the yarn extends to 5,0. This indicates that all the liquid from the 5-quart container has been poured into the 7-quart container. In any pouring, one container must be filled to the brim or another emptied completely, for there is no other way to be sure of the contents of each, since there are no markings on the vessels.

The yarn describes the steps, giving the amounts in the 7- and the 5-quart containers in that order: 0,0; 0,5; 5,0; 5,5; 7,3; 0,3; 3,0; 3,5; 7,1; 0,1; 1,0; 1,5; 6,0. Look at the change from 3,5 to 7,1. You must fill the 7-quart container using the 5-quart container. Only 4 quarts may be transferred, and this leaves 1 quart remaining in the 5-quart vessel. The 6,0 point represents the end of the yarn's work because the 7-quart container now holds 6 quarts, the 5-quart container is empty, and the 12-quart container must hold the other 6 quarts. This is the required division of the liquid into two equal parts.

This same problem can also be solved by first moving horizontally from the 0,0 point. This would be the same as filling the 7-quart container first. The yarn gives a second sequence of pourings. Compare the two results to determine which first step leads to the least number of pourings.

Now let the yarn solve another problem. The only restriction is that the capacity of the largest vessel must be as large or larger than the capacities of the other two combined. Let the containers be of 8-, 5-, and 3-quart capacity. The problem is to divide the contents of the 8-quart vessel into 4-quart portions. The markers on the board are now repositioned to limit the travels of the yarn to a portion that is five spaces across and three spaces high.

Try inventing some problems of your own and solve these by using the yarn and computing board. Are there certain divisions of the liquid that are impossible to obtain? How might you find out?

As a final problem, let us try to determine why the computing board works so well. First, we should understand why the yarn must travel according to the prescribed rules. The yarn must always travel from one boundary of the parallelogram to another boundary because one or the other of the two smaller vessels is either filled or emptied completely in each pouring. Moreover, the yarn must follow a line of nails set in one of three possible directions. This comes about either because the contents of one of the smaller vessels does not change or because the increase in the content of one is matched by the decrease in the other. When the yarn reaches one of the boundaries, it may retrace its path, move along the boundary toward one of the vertices of the parallelogram, or reflect like a ray of light. The first two alternatives must be excluded—why?—leaving the only route for the yarn the one already described.

We now know why the yarn must move the way it does, but how does it find the answer to a problem? The yarn moves from boundary to boundary, exhausting all possible answers, until it comes to the answer for which you have been looking. Clever? Yes. But completely lacking an intelligence of its own.

Format by Kohar Alexanian

Composed and bound by American Book–Stratford Press, Inc.

Printed by The Murray Printing Co.

HARPER & ROW, PUBLISHERS, INC.